Tree Farm Girl

Tree Farm Girl

By

Ernesto Alaniz

Ernesto Alaniz

Tree Farm Girl

ISBN: Paperback: 978-1-7323579-0-7

Published by Hidden Hollows Publishing
Hiddenhollows.net

Printed in the United States of America
2018

To Angie.
My Tree Farm Girl.

Ernesto Alaniz

ACKNOWLEDGEMENTS

A special thanks to Mark Aardsma, Alexa Boersen, Ron Gjelhaug, Scott and Mariah Gordon, Justin Lawes, John Rooney, and Mike Struckman. You are truly patrons of the arts.

A special nod to the music of Rich Mullins. It gave me a language that I am still speaking.

A WORD BEFORE

"How did you two meet?"

It's an inevitable question and a common one, as a couple moves through life and encounters new people over the course of 15 years of marriage. Every time it comes up we exchange a look and smile. "It's a long story…"

The telling of the tale is always fun. My husband knows how to spin a yarn, as they say, in all its dramatic glory. He is the master storyteller, I am the editorial heckler, interjecting corrections and snarky quips, all in good fun. I imagine it's a bit like listening to an old couple reminiscing and trying to recount the details of a lifetime together – only hopefully less frustrating for everyone.

But we've always told the story this way. Ernesto sets the stage and paints the picture; I add my amendments. At particularly dramatic moments in the tale, people often turn to me in astonishment and ask, "What did you think of all this?" Here is where I will tell you, if you want to know.

Throughout this book, there will be an occasional addendum, notes (in italics) at the end of a chapter. This is my take on the subject. It may at times recast the scene in a new light, for, as we always say, perception is a very powerful thing. But this is how I saw things, my two cents. For what it's worth.

-Angie Alaniz

Tree Farm Girl

Pure Michigan

Michigan is the greatest state in the Union. There are many who will argue the point, and they are wrong. Here in our great state we have lakes, and trees, and wildlife. There are four distinct seasons that mark the passing of time. Every September, Michigan flexes her muscles, offering a myriad of colors to line every highway. Come December, the snow falls. Winter is a long, hard stretch for those who call the mitten home. But it is a necessary evil. The cold keeps the spiders from becoming tarantulas and the snakes, pythons. The freeze has another benefit: the thaw. Death is necessary to witness resurrection.

Every year the green comes back. Flowers blossom, and the birds return. The sun rises once again, and a song is found on the lips of all God's creatures. The Spring springs us forward to Summer. No school and no worries. A time to drive and play and fall in love.

It was a Michigan summer I fell in love. It was a different summer when she would follow me down. And yet one more to make it go. This is that story as best as I can remember it.

PART ONE

SUMMER 2001

The Wilderness

"I knew from a young age that my parents prayed for my future husband."
  -Angela Sims

I was lying in a pool of blood and water when I called on the name of Jesus.

"Help. Anyone. Someone." I knew my cries were worthless. The large walk-in cooler was designed to insulate, and the same technology that protected the cold from the heat also absorbed any sound. Still I cried out. I needed my boss, Casanova, to walk through that door. I needed to be found. I needed someone strong who could pick up this crate off my broken body.

It was cold lying face-up in this cooler. The water was only an inch deep, but it had recently been ice, so it was freezing. The fans blew constantly, adding to the chill. There was no one coming. I lifted my head to see my situation. Covering my chest and midsection were crates of raw chicken. They had been packed in ice, so it looked like an avalanche of drumsticks had found me unawares. I had been carrying two cases of the raw meat when it happened. I always liked carrying two cases. I was the only guy on staff who could do it, and I thought it impressed the girls. Stupid. I had grabbed the cases, lifted, and begun to walk to the large door in order to exit. But I slipped. I stepped on an ice cube and my foot slid out from beneath me. I tried to recover, but I had an extra forty pounds in my arms. As I tried to readjust for weight, my bad knee popped. They say it tears. It doesn't sound like a tear. It sounds like a pop. Like sticking your thumb in your cheek and darting it out. When the knee gave way, I fell back, and those cases came tumbling after.

I lay there, half buried in ice, on my back in water, the only cook on duty during morning prep. It could be hours before someone came back to check on me. I began pushing the cases off my body. I had to clear the wreckage. I had to see the damage for myself. I could feel that something was wrong in my left leg. But I had to see it with my own eyes. In horror movies, the girl always goes upstairs to check out the noise. People always yell at the TV, saying how unrealistic such a thing is. I keep quiet, because I would go. I have to know. Is it a murderous clown, or did I just leave the sink running? Only one way to find out.

I pushed the ice off me and saw it. At the knee, my leg shot out at a sick unnatural angle. The pain should be horrific, but I was covered in ice and sitting in a cooler, so I couldn't feel much of anything. I laid my head back down in the water. I stared up at the ceiling fan, thinking about the summer that was passing.

I had been in Texas now for 5 months. I had a trailer all set up on my grandmother's land. It had power, water, and I had tarped off the roof to keep the rain out. I had a job, a library card, and even some good family near. But I was in hiding. I had come here to hide from the God of heaven. I had driven through the biggest snow storm I had ever seen, fighting my way out of Chicago, to get as far away as I could from my mother, my church, and especially Him. I thought Jesus had failed me, and I was dead-set on failing Him.

He chased me to Texas. He chased me into this freezer. He was calling me home.

"Help. Anyone. Someone." Still, nothing. My body was shaking from the cold. But there was heat. I tried to blink it away. But my eyes kept pooling with warm water. When the pool got too deep, a drop would overflow down past my ears. The path would wind its way through beard and stubble to find the sea. Then the pool flooded. There had been months of distraction. Months of keeping my head down and trying to avoid the Great I Am. I had played out my last chance, every road was now a dead end. There was only one way to see; I had to look up. I spoke into the darkness. "Okay. I yield. I'll go back. I'll come home."

The darkness scattered as the big walk-in door swung open. A young Latina stood there staring at the wreckage around me. She ran from the freezer screaming for help. The door was still open, and I was bathed in light.

The Wrong Door

"God, if you ever want me to get married, you are gonna have to bring him to my front door."

-Angela Sims

I was almost asleep when the home phone rang. Instinctively, I shot awake and threw my legs off the bed. The pain was immediate and severe. The knee was still wrapped after the reconstructive surgery, and bending it was still very mechanical. I grabbed my thigh and grimaced in the dark, cursing the low throb. The first ring ended, and the second began. I got to my feet and hopped to the bottom of the basement stairs. I had to get to the phone now. It threatened to wake the whole house. So I limped up the stairs as fast as I could, enduring the hurt each footfall would bring. The second ring ended as I threw open the basement door. I could see the phone now. It was attached to a wall, only eight feet from where I stood. The third ring had just begun to engage when I grabbed it off its cradle.

"Hello?" I spoke in a panicked whisper.

The voice on the other end of the phone was one I had not heard in nearly a year. "Nesto?" It was my good friend, the lovable vagabond, AC Crumpton.

"Dude! Where are you?"

"I'm in Michigan, man. I'm like an hour north of you."

"Dude, how long you been in town?"

"I've been here for like a month."

The answer stung. It had been a hard month, and I had been alone. But, he was here now, and that would have to be good enough. "So what's up, man?"

"I need you to come up here." He sounded scared.

"Now?"

"Yeah. Now."

"Are you okay?"

"No man. I've been reading Nabokov."

My tone changed instantly. I understood the gravity of the situation. We had made a pact, Adam and I. Due to the nature of the Russian's skill paired with his moral ambiguity, we had created rules. Never read him at night. Never read him alone. Adam had broken both rules, and his mind was in trouble. "I'm on my way."

When I hung up the phone, the house was once again plunged into silence. I listened hard. I didn't hear anyone stirring. Maybe this call wouldn't bring any morning wrath. I looked at the open basement door. There was no way I was going down the stairs again. My knee was on fire, and the stairs were too loud. I had to get out of here before someone woke up and I got pulled into a thing. I was clothed in a Hanes white tank and some well worn boxers. I shrugged. It was just Adam. No reason to dress up. At the door I looked around for some shoes. Nothing. My sandals were downstairs. Once again, I shrugged. Who needs shoes anyway? I held my breath at the front door, and then flipped the deadbolt. I swung the door open and stepped into a cool summer's night. I closed the front door quickly (but quietly) and tested the knob. Locked. I let the screen door close as lightly as possible. I was out. I was free. I limped across the front yard to The Beast. The '89 Astro Van was awful to look at and worse to drive. But she was mine. I had bought her years earlier for $1 from a pastor in town. And tonight she had to bring me to the heart of the Thumb, to a small little town called Kingston.

The drive north was scary. It was foggy, and I was driving too fast on roads I did not know. But I was in a hurry. The voice on the phone was in need, and I wished to answer the call quickly. So I drove hard and true. My newly acquired Bruce Springsteen live tape wailed out on the radio, and his walk into the night matched my own.

I came to the place I sought 2 hours later. It was in middle-of-nowhere Michigan, right where AC said it would be. It was dark and really late... well after midnight. I was barefoot, boxer clad, and bound in a nasty old comforter of questionable origins. I pulled over on the side of the road and stared. In front of me was a large 4' x 8' sign announcing that I had found Hidden Hollows Tree Farm. It stood right in front of a dirt road that led deeply into forest. The small lane winded impossibly out of sight, but here near the road there were two attaching driveways. To the left sat an old abandoned cabin from an earlier time. It looked unlivable, so I pulled in and parked in front of her. I got out of the van and stepped into the quiet country night. I didn't like this at all. There was no neighborhood in the city of Flint that I feared after dark. But the country was a different story. There were animals in these woods. Bears maybe. Not only that, but I wondered of rednecks waiting to find a lost Latino in their dastardly traps. I approached the old farmhouse and peered into the windows. No one home.

AC had said he was staying right off the road, by the big sign. I should be close. I crossed the small lane and walked up the right side driveway. There was a house that looked lived in, but there were no lights ablaze. I knocked on the door. Nothing. I looked around in the darkness. I really didn't like this. I tried the handle, and the door opened. I called out, "AC?" Nothing. I put a foot in the door, cried out again. "AC, you here?" Still, nothing. As I stood there, one foot in and one foot out, I could see myself in one of the horror movies I hated so much as a child. The murderer was probably waiting for me in a closet. Or behind the shower curtain.

Walking around in my underwear on a cool summer's night was not what I had signed up for. I wanted to leave. I had no way to contact my friend, no way to call back and ask for better directions. I had only two choices. I could follow this road further into Hidden Hollows, or drive all the way back to Waterford. I stared down the road, cursing its disappearance into darkness. I pulled my blanket tighter around myself and began to walk.

The night was cold, and I should have been too. But the sweat flowed freely. Every step I took down that road was a fight. I didn't know where I was walking. I feared knives and teeth and guns. What if I stumbled upon someone sleeping in their home? They could shoot me dead, and ain't no jury in the world gonna second-guess them. What was I doing sneaking around their land in the middle of the night? And why wasn't I wearing pants?

It felt like an hour that I trekked down that small dirt lane, and finally I began to see light in the trees ahead. The road ended in a cul-de-sac, passing in front of a single large house. It was magnificent. I could see that even in the darkness. Light shone from different sides of it, from different levels. A mansion in the woods in the dead of night. And there were lights on. This was a horrible idea.

I walked on. I followed the road, then the foot path, and finally stepped onto a large concrete porch. I wished it was wood. At least that way it would creak underneath my weight, announcing my arrival. I sighed strongly. This had to be the house. There was nowhere else. So I reached out and knocked on the door. And of course, it was the wrong door.

I looked around, trying to play casual. I really wanted to look like I wasn't scared out of my head. Finally, the door opened. And it was not AC. No. I had come to the wrong house that night. Standing before me was a young woman who didn't seem the least surprised to see me. "Hello?" she said.

I stood there embarrassed and at a loss for words. I was all of a sudden very aware of my appearance and lack of clothing. The hair on my head was long and unkempt. I looked like some homeless dreg wandering the woods in search of food. In front of me stood a very respectable kind-faced lady who didn't seem at all afraid to have a 300-pound Mexican on her porch.

That was the night I met Angela Kaye Sims. Turns out, it was the right door after all.

While wandering around unknown territory in the dark was understandably unnerving, from inside the well-lit, cozy house, this scene takes on an entirely different tone. It was not unusual for there to be people at my parents' house until well into the night; on this particular day, we'd had several young adults over from church, some of whom were still there. Having someone else show up at such a late hour was not surprising in the least, even if he was barefoot and wrapped in a blanket. We opened the door wide, and he came in to join the party. (And if you know Ernesto, you know the party was better for it.)

Reading Books Alone Together

"The house was always full of people. It's why we built it."
-Angela Sims

It was the wrong house, but the right place. Adam indeed was living on their property. That house back near the road was a duplex. He was living on the backside of it. I found him that night and there was much rejoicing.

The morning came and revealed Hidden Hollows for something more. It didn't seem like a farm, for I didn't see tractors or workers. It wasn't a camp, for there were no dorms or campers. We walked down the long driveway, only this time I was not afraid.

"So, what are you doing here?"

Adam replied, "I needed a place to live. They had a bed."

"You working?"

"Naw."

"You paying these guys rent?"

"I hope not."

I laughed. Not a real laugh. But a placeholder. "How long you gonna be here?"

"Until I leave."

I enjoyed the banter for a while, but eventually I always got annoyed. So I pushed a little.

"Your mom know you're back?"

Adam gave no answer. It was a lousy thing to do, bringing that up. There was a reason we were friends. For us, home was just another place where we were strangers. We lived on the road, thumbs up and hopeful that someone would pull over and give us a ride. Alas, we had no idea where we were going.

I moved on. "Who are these people?"

"The Sims."

"And…"

"They are good people." Adam believed there was none good but God, so this got my attention. For him, this was high praise indeed.

The house was in view now. It was larger than it looked in the dark. I actually couldn't get a full view of it from the front. It was so wide I couldn't see how far it went back.

"They know we're coming?"

"Naw."

"What does this guy do?"

"He builds log homes."

I nodded. That explained the wonder that stood before me. "Cool."

"Yeah. And I don't know if you've noticed, but we're surrounded by Christmas trees."

I hadn't. I turned to my right, and then my left, and sure enough, we were between fields of pine and fir. "Way cool."

We approached the house. Above the porch there were words carved on a plaque. It read, "Say Among the Nations The Lord Reigns." I stood underneath that sign staring at it. That was a heck of a thing to place over the entrance to a home. I wondered who could live up to such a thing.

Adam held open the screen door for me. "Welcome to Hidden Hollows."

I walked in, and there was a fuzzy silence. There was the sound of life, but not the sound of conversation. I walked on carefully, and we both remained silent, as though walking on some sacred ground. In front of me was a hallway to the kitchen, with another small hallway to the right. I took the turn and descended the five steps down into the great room. Now, I have never understood this term, "great room". I had never used it, and when I'd come across it, I would furrow my brow. But now I understood. This was truly a great room. It was easily larger than any trailer I had lived in growing up. The ceiling rose twelve feet into the air, with large wooden chandeliers bringing a soft light. The entire western wall was made up of windows between large crossing beams. Outside the windows was forest, which somehow made the room feel even larger.

A large couch served as a dividing wall, effectively cutting the room in half. It separated a music studio on the far end from a semicircle of seats around a large fireplace. There was a television there, but it was not the center. It was an afterthought. This was not a room for watching. This was a room for music, and conversation, and the changing of lives.

In the Great Room sat three of the Sims clan. There was Bob, who then (and now) looked like Eric Clapton from his *Chronicles* record. He was reading a travel magazine. On the couch that was a wall sat his wife, Mrs. Kaye. She was reading a book on a foreign culture, highlighter in hand. And on the chair nearest me sat the girl from last night, Angela. She was still in her pajamas, and the steaming coffee at her side told me that her day was still young. In her hands was a paperback called *Trekking in the Nepal Himalaya*.

As we entered, Bob looked up and spoke, with a bit of a grin. "Hello. It's family reading hour. Feel free to pull up a book and join us."

Adam had his book by Nabokov, the book that brought me up here in the middle of the night. I was unarmed. I sat on some pillows near the fireplace and stared in awe at the people around me. How could I have known there was a place in the world where families sat together in silence? No. Not in silence. Under the turning of pages there was a song playing just a little too loud. I had never imagined such a place. I sat there and drank it all in. I didn't know what this was, but I liked it.

With no book to take my mind, I listened to the song that was playing. I knew it, but didn't know it. A man with a tortured soul sang about a girl in a car in a parking lot, and she was thinking of jumping. She was sick and tired of life. And then he sang the line, "We're all sick and tired of something."

My eyes misted over. My knee ached. I looked around at a life I had never known. "Yeah, man," I thought to myself. "We sure are."

Road Trip

"The earth expanding right hand and left hand,
   The picture alive, every part in its best light,
   The music falling in where it is wanted,
   and stopping where it is not wanted
   Oh highway I travel...
   You express me better than I can express myself,
   You shall be more to me than my poem."
   -Walt Whitman, in "Song of the Open Road"
   (as recorded in Angie's journal, October 2001)

Chicago was a wound. It had been a mistake coming here.
Standing in the student drop-off at the Moody Bible Institute
reminded me of the life I had forfeited. I hadn't stepped foot
on campus grounds since I washed out nine months ago. But
Adam had a plane to catch, and I wanted to be there to say
goodbye.

It had been a good month on the tree farm. I came up
every weekend to see my friend. We read and dreamed and
would talk about the will of God and souls of men. I had
even come prepared for a couple of family reading hours.
The Brothers Karamazov was almost finished. Now Adam was
leaving as quickly as he had arrived. He was flying down to
Mexico to serve under a local evangelist.

"It's been a good month, man."

26

"Yeah."

We were good at being friends, but terrible at being people. We didn't know how to say the things.

With that, Adam walked away. I limped back to the car. The limp was more pronounced than it had been a minute ago. It wasn't my leg that hurt. It was my life. I barely had a foundation set. My life was without form and void. That is fine with a friend to share it, but mine just left. I was once again alone.

At the car waiting was a girl. There stood Angie. She had been in the city visiting her sister. She needed a ride home, and I was going her way. I looked at her there, and I was sour. Why the crap did I agree to this? I was emotionally spent and did not want to make small talk with some girl I barely knew. Normally, I could carry six hours of conversation. But not today. I needed an empty car and my beloved cassettes. I needed some speed and freedom to untangle the lies.

"You ready to go?"

"Yup. All loaded."

We both got into my big Astro Van. I climbed into the blue captain's chair with keys in hand, and I just sat there. I couldn't do this. I looked over. "Angie?"

"Yeah?"

"I am really sad. And I don't feel like talking. I just want to drive and listen to music. Is that cool?"

"That's fine."

I studied her face. Usually fine wasn't fine. Fine was usually just a placeholder for all kinds of awful subtext. It was the non-verbals that told you the truth. But I didn't read any cues from her. Her "fine" was actually fine.

"Thanks."

I reached down between us and scanned the cassettes. The case was full of EA originals. There was not a single store bought tape in my collection. Today's tape... What Susan Said. This was an album full of loss. This was perfect.

Mile after mile, tape after tape, the radio sang. And so did I. I sang like she wasn't even there. For the record, I am not a good singer. I obeyed the bumper sticker and sang like no one was listening. And why not? After dropping Angie off, I would never see her again. With Adam gone, I had no reason to go back up to the tree farm. That outpost of heaven was being closed to me.

Five hours in and Bruce Springsteen's "Jungleland" was coming to a close. My heart was no longer overflowing. I had exorcised the demons. And that's when I saw Angie. This poor woman. She had just driven across the state with a tone-deaf psycho belting out sad pop songs. She didn't deserve this.

"You hungry?"

"Yeah."

"I know just the place. You like Mexican?"

"Who doesn't?"

"My mom makes the best beans in Metro Detroit. You wanna have some authentic Mexican cuisine before you head back?"

"Sounds great."

I kept the car headed east and passed by the turn north. I was bringing the girl home. Might as well talk a little.

"So, you know any of those songs?"

"I knew a lot of them."

"Cool. You ever... you know... make a mixed tape?"

She smiled. It was a really good smile. There was a story behind it. "Yeah, I've made a few."

"Maybe someday we'll share another drive and listen to one."

"That'd be great."

Silence. That's all I had. I was already out of ammo.

Thankfully, she continued. "You know what's just as fun as making tapes?"

"What's that?"

"Dubbing movies."

It was my turn to be lost. "I don't follow."

"You know how on those CD/tape decks, how you turn the CD on and then hit record to get the sound on the tape?"

"I'm following."

"Well, imagine playing a movie through a video camera to your TV. It's the same thing. You just hook up a mic to the recorder and record audio over the spot you want to dub."

"Ok. But why would you want to dub over a movie?"

"My dad used to do it with my sisters and me. We would make R-rated movies PG so he could show them to youth group."

"No way. That is really funny."

"Yeah. I think *Speed* was the best one we ever did. We still watch that one and laugh like crazy."

"That is one of the goofiest things I've ever heard." And honestly, it was. It was creative and funny and familial. It was pitch perfect.

"Maybe someday you can come up and watch it with everyone. It's gotta be around there somewhere."

"That'd be cool."

We pulled into my mother's driveway, and I knew right away she wasn't home. "Well, you're gonna have to wait on that Mexican food. Looks like mi madre is not home."

"No hay problema, hermano."

I jumped out of the van. "Your Spanish sounds great. What gives?"

"I lived in the Dominican Republic for a year when I was thirteen. Then I spent a semester abroad in Costa Rica."

"Hold that thought." I opened the door and stuck my head in. "Ma. Mom. You home?" I looked at Angie. "We ain't having Mexican. But I can make us some dinner. You game?"

"Sure."

We entered the house. I went to the freezer to see what we had for food. Fish fillets. Frozen broccoli. Canned corn. Groovy.

"So, how'd you end up in the D.R.?"

"It's a long story."

"Good thing this oven has a long pre-heat."

She relented. "Well, our church is part of the Missionary Church denomination. And every year they have this big family camp for all the churches in the state."

"Family camp?"

"Yeah. Families all have trailers on the property, or cabins, or drive in an RV for the 10-day event. There is chapel every night, and every year there is one service set aside for missions. There would be a guest speaker, usually music in a foreign language, and then a call to give your life for foreign missions. Well, my mom and dad always used to talk about how someday, when we were all grown up and gone, they were going to go overseas and serve. One year, during the invitation, my sisters and I decided we didn't like that plan. During the altar call, we girls went to their seats and told them we didn't want to wait. We wanted to go with them. So we all as a family went up and committed ourselves to the mission field. A year later, we were living in the Dominican Republic."

I could see the scene in my mind's eye. Three pre-teen girls marching up to their parents and demanding a life of faith.

"That's an amazing story Ang."

She smiled and shrugged.

The oven dinged, and I prepared our plates. The food was not good. But it was not bad either. I put on some Mozart for background noise, and we sat to eat.

"So, what was it like living in the D.R.?"

"It changed my life. Seeing true poverty that young. Seeing the church impoverished but strong. I think that changed the whole course of my life. I ended up studying sociology and missions in college. I've been leading teams for over 2 years now. It's why I didn't date in college. It's why I quit my job as a builder and became a full-time missionary at my church."

She wasn't bragging. Sh was just sharing. But the sharing was a bright light that filled my vision. And just like that, this girl who had been a burden became something else. I was aware of her. I saw her.

After dinner, we began the drive north. I put on a tape, but I turned the volume down. I was inviting conversation, and I was not disappointed.

"So, what's with the cane?"

I looked down at the cane resting between our seats. "Just in case my knee acts up."

"I've never seen you use it."

"I'd rather limp."

"So what happened?"

I looked over at her. An hour ago, I would've ducked the question. But I was enjoying this. "Me and God got in a wrestling match. I lost."

"So, what? You Jacob or something?"

I kept my eyes on the road, but I stole a glance. She was quick. And she was knowledgeable.

"Yeah, that's it exactly."

"What were you wrestling about?"

I laughed aloud.

"Is that a funny question?"

"Forgive me. I am not laughing at you or because of you. I am just really enjoying the drive."

"Okay." She didn't push. She instead waited for an answer.

"Angie, a few years back, my family went through something really bad. And it knocked me down. It was just too much. So I shut down. I stopped going to my classes. I stopped going to work. I stopped going to church. One day I just crawled under my bed and stayed there for a few weeks. My roommate would bring me food, and I'd shower once in a while. But mainly I just slept and tried to avoid feeling anything."

It is an odd thing, telling someone your story. It forces you to remember, to feel afresh the pain of yesterday.

"I ended up getting fired. My church let me go as their youth pastor. And I failed out of college. I took off down to Texas to hide out for awhile. And I didn't come home until He took my knee away." Unconsciously, my hand began to massage my knee, remembering the wound.

"I remember telling God, 'I am not mad at you, but I don't want to talk to you anymore.' And I didn't. And I haven't. Honestly, in a lot of ways, I am still under that bed."

I stopped talking. I had said more than I ever intended to share. I looked over and saw a tear rolling down Angie's face. She spoke. "That is really sad."

"Yeah, I guess it is."

I reached out and turned the volume up a little. It was time to retreat. Silence reigned from Auburn Hills all the way to Imlay City.

"Ernesto?"

I turned the volume down again. "Yeah?"

"You know, my dad mentors young men. It's what he does. It's why he gave Adam a bed. Maybe you could talk with him."

"Maybe."

And we left it at that.

As we turned off the highway, the thought came back to me. I had no reason to come back to Hidden Hollows Tree Farm. I had no peoples here anymore. With AC gone, I now had no reason to come north. I was a stranger to this beautiful land. And that made me sad. This place had felt like home, and I hadn't known that feeling for a very long time.

I walked in with her to give thanks to the Simses for their hospitality. Alas, they were not home.

"Angie, can I have some paper? I want to leave a note for your parents."

"Sure." Angie found paper and pen and gave it to me.

I stared at the empty piece of paper. It was an easy note to write. "To Mr. and Mrs. Sims. Thank you for your kindness and hospitality these last few weeks. Your home has been a home to me. -Ernesto." But that is not what I wrote. What came from my hand was something else entirely.

"Mr. Bob. I have no father. Could I come and see you again? I would like to learn how to be a good man. Like you." I attached my phone number, put the note on the fridge, and then drove away, not knowing if I would see the Sims ever again.

This is one of the stories whose telling always seems to beg the question: "What did Angie think of all this?" And this is one of those instances in which my noticeably lacking flair for the dramatic is sure to disappoint. Because the answer is, quite simply, I didn't think anything of it. A friend requesting silence on a sad day for a long drive seemed like the most natural thing in the world. I had recently endured a similar disappointment, and I understood that grieving the absence of a dear friend sometimes calls for the healing power of a little bit of a time and some familiar songs.

I suppose this is one of the ways in which Ernesto and I are perfectly suited for one another. It's difficult to describe to someone who doesn't know us well, because we are so utterly different in many ways, but so alike in so many ways that matter. He tends to express himself in a big way, while it has been said of me that if I appeared any more calm, I'd be dead. But we both appreciate, at its proper time, "the bliss of solitude," as Wordsworth would call it. So, on this day, it made perfect sense that he'd want some time to be alone with his thoughts.

Also, some good tunes and the open road is a special kind of joy for a contemplative type like myself. I thought it was a great trip. In fact, I wrote about the drive in my journal: "It was such a pleasant trip home with Ernesto... I so enjoyed his company that it seemed like the quickest trip back from Chicago as opposed to the longest."

And for the record, he's not tone-deaf. That might have actually made the trip miserable.

Father Figure

"The world is all messed up and love is so hard to have because it has to fight through many prisons and much pain."

-Ernesto Alaniz, in an email to Angie (May, 2002)

Bob called the next day.

"Ernesto, you are more than welcome to come here as often as you would like. And if you want to pray, I would gladly pray with you." The invitation was given. And at first, I didn't come.

When my knee gave out, I had come back to the land of my salvation. This is where I had met Jesus. This is where I had found my calling. I had come back, however, not a conquering hero, but a wounded deserter.

I had been the first kid in my family to go to college. I was also the first to come home a college dropout. Before I'd set out, my church had laid hands on me in prayer. They had given money so I could go to college. That investment ended with me managing a restaurant on the main strip back home. In the faces of friends and acquaintances there was the question, "What happened to you?"

I endured the stares. I faced family, and I faced my church. But I had not yet faced the Lord. I was finally going to church again. But I was the worst kind of churchgoer. I sat in the back row, arms crossed, daring the preacher to challenge me. I found fault with the worship leaders, with the megachurch that I called home, with the preacher, with everything. I was proud, and I was angry. I blamed everyone and everything for my current position in life.

In the mornings, I would read. Through all my newfound cynicism, some part of me wanted to find the way back to Narnia.

One morning, I opened up the Bible. And there was this story of a son. After taking his father's wealth, he goes away and wastes it on riotous living. When the party ends, he finds himself in need. He has no money. He has no job. He's in a far country doing things that he had been taught never to do. And one day he wakes up. He comes to himself. It's like a light clicks on and he is aware of who he is and who his father is. He realizes that at home even the servants eat well. So he begins the long walk home. He walks home barefoot and dirty. The whole journey he keeps practicing his speech. He has this great fear of being rejected, so he has to make sure his argument is a good one. Finally, he can see his father's house. He has come back to the land that was once home. But he is changed. He is no longer the child of promise. He is a failure. He is the fool. He is the great disappointment. Off in the distance, he can see his old man on the porch. And that old man begins to run towards him.

I came back to my mother, and she embraced me.

I came back to my church, and they didn't slam the door in my face.

But how do you come back to God? How can you repay what was so richly given and so carelessly squandered?

I looked down to the Bible again. The son launches into his speech. "I am no longer worthy to be called your son." That's right. I am no longer worthy. "Let me be as one of your servants." That seems fair. It's why I had come back here. To just get a job, go to church, and go through the motions. But the father doesn't hear the excuses. He embraces his son. He cries out commands at the servants. He tells them to bring shoes. He tells them to prepare a feast of celebration. I can imagine their confusion. Why? Why kill the fatted calf for this failure? Why rejoice over this son who has wasted the Father's gifts on his own pleasure? The father tells them why. "For this my son was dead, and is alive again; he was lost, and is found."

The father doesn't stand there with face resolute. He doesn't demand tribute or groveling. He hugs his lost son. He puts shoes on his dirty feet. He puts a robe to cover his nakedness. And on his hand he does not put the brand of a servant, but the royal ring of sonship.

Have you ever held the pieces together for too long? Have you ever pushed down all the hurt and fear and just ignored it? You think you got it all locked away in the box. But the box cracks. It's just too much. I felt it give way. The lock broke asunder. The anger gave way to guilt and remorse. I was the boy who ran away. I was the boy who had been enslaved. I had run from everyone I ever loved. It was time to come home.

The dam broke, and I wept like a child. I called on the name of the Lord. I apologized. I told him all the things. It just poured out. And when the well ran dry, I knew what I needed to do. I got in my van and I began to drive north. I wanted to be near someone who knew the way. I needed a guide, someone to push and pull. Bob knew the way. He talked to God the way a musician plays piano. The truly gifted don't try to play, they just play. The practice and the familiarity make it effortless. Bob didn't try to talk to God.

He just talked to Him. Like talking to a guy in the seat next to you.

I drove north with hope in my heart. I was ready. I found Bob in the kitchen, cleaning up after lunch. "Hey Bob, I was wondering if you had time to pray?" I was horribly awkward. But I was there. I had come to myself. I wanted to be near my Father once again. And this was a step in that direction.

We prayed together that day. A week later, I showed up again. Sunday after Sunday, I made the ninety-minute drive. The tree farm was not my church. It was my prayer closet. This was the burning bush on the Mount of God. Every week we sat out near the Big Rock behind the house. There was no curriculum. There was no plan. We just talked about life for a while. Then we would be silent together.

Coming home is really hard. It felt impossible. But the Father was waiting for me. He waits for all His children.

The Mexican

"As for admiration, it was always very welcome when it came, but she did not depend on it."
  -Jane Austen in *Northanger Abbey*

It takes a special kind of fool to try and solve the question of love in the world. And I was such a fool. So was AC.

"It's what we're looking for. It's that thing in a woman that sets her apart from all other women. Not her hair, not her lips, nor any makeup she may or may not be wearing. This is her luminescent self, shining brightly among the dross. This is what we call the Wow. It is the lightning bolt. It is the force of personality. It is greatness. And not everyone has it. But when you see it, you can't help but be in awe of it. It is this we seek."

I pushed for more. "But doesn't it fade? Is this really in her, or is it just you being intoxicated by the thought of her? This Wow is gonna go away as soon as you see that she's a normal person."

Adam wouldn't be moved. "No. This is something she possesses. And it does not fade over time. It was there before you, and will be there after. It is an Eternal Wow."

"Eternal Wow." I liked it. And since that conversation had by two 18-year-old boys, I had been on the lookout for the

39

Eternal Wow everywhere I went. I even had a bunch of tests to see whether the Wow faded or was within her.

My first and most important test was one of the mind. I would ask a girl the all-important question, "What are your top three favorite movies?" This is a seemingly harmless question, but it reveals much. If there was a Bruckheimer film on the list, the Wow diminished. If her list was merely entertainment, the Wow diminished. If she couldn't name three movies, the Wow diminished.

"Angie?"

"Yeah?"

It was a Sunday evening on the tree farm, and I was still around.

"What are your top three favorite movies?"

She thought about it. "How about my top three favorite books?"

I sat up. This was a better question. "That sounds like a novel idea."

"Okay, in no particular order. I'm gonna say *Hinds Feet on High Places*. It's an allegory I have always liked. And then, I'd have to go with *Little Women*. It's a story about sisters, and that is a story I have lived out and understand."

I nodded. I had not read any of these books. But I was aware of them.

"And my all-time favorite would have to be *Jane Eyre*."

"I've never heard of it."

"You should give it a read." For the first time in a long time, I found myself out of my literary element. I hadn't read a single one of the works that had shaped this woman's soul. That would not stand. On the way home, I stopped by Borders Booksellers and grabbed a copy of *Jane Eyre*. I began reading it that night. Jane Eyre is unlike any female character I have ever read. Actually, I had been reading a lot of Hemingway, and his women are always in orbit around men. But Jane, she stood powerfully against the conventions I was exposed to. She was not ruled by her feelings. They were there, and they were strong and feminine. But her mind was sharp. She knew who she was, and she had a profound respect for the truth. So when her feelings ran against truth and righteousness, she chose truth. She would choose against her emotions. She could turn down a suitor even though it would have meant financial stability. She could turn down true love because it was not hers to take. She would leave home for that home to be preserved. I read of her, and I began to be drawn to her. And at the end, when Jane was a beacon of the Eternal Wow us boys had dreamed of for so long, I realized my predicament. Angie was Jane Eyre.

Angie had graduated college and had wanted so badly to serve the global church. For a year she applied for jobs with a variety of organizations. The rejection letters all bled together. They wanted someone who was married. They wanted nannies for missionary kids. The roles she felt called to were withheld from her. So she spent years working on her father's crew, building log homes and paying down college debt.

Suitors had come for her. Stories of old were told by family and friends, and I gleaned the details. There had been a suitor who brought a ring. But she knew he had not come for her. He had come for a wife. He didn't care who it was, it just had to be a girl who had similar morals. She could've had the wedding, the celebration, the house, all of it. But she walked away. She wanted to be loved for who she was. She didn't want to be a wife. She wanted to be Angie, loved for her mind and soul. Three times she told him no. When, just a few months after the final profession and proposal, he was engaged to another girl, she knew she had done the right thing. She would rather be alone than have less than love.

Years wore on, and doors did not open for her. But she was faithful. Eventually, she left the log home crew. She felt the Lord calling her to serve her small country church full-time as a missionary. She did not do this blindly. She simplified her life and began to give her time and gifts to the church. She led the worship team once a month. She began leading the youth group on Wednesday nights. She began leading teams overseas, exposing American kids to the whole wide world. And it was here I had met her. A woman four years my senior. A woman content to serve God with no fanfare. A woman waiting on no man, for she had found her hope in Him.

I saw her, and I recognized her, but I could not have her. She was formed. She was beautiful and good. I was still broken. I did not yet know how to love anything more than myself. I had to be good with God before I could ever be good with a woman. I had to find my way in the world. I had to walk the path that had been shown to me all those years ago.

Two weeks passed before I appeared on the Sims' porch again. I pulled into the tree farm that night a compromised man. I knew what I had to do. But it was going to be hard to do it.

There were many people at the Sims household this night. Hidden Hollows was a place anyone was welcome, where everyone belonged. I entered to the sound of voices being silenced. The lights were out in the great room and a movie was beginning. I stuck my head in.

"Ernesto!" I was known here. I was enjoyed and accepted.

"Hey, everybody. What you watching?"

A voice from the crowd spoke, "The Mexican."

"Cool."

I pushed up against the side walls and sprung myself out of the room. I had not come for a movie, I had come to make an announcement.

Bob was sitting at the table eating cake. I think this is one of Bob's favorite things, making wonderful desserts and then enjoying them. I grabbed a plate and joined him. I couldn't let him eat alone.

From my seat I could see down the length of the hallway to the front entry. From the adjoining hall which led to the great room, Angie appeared. She was leaving the crowd when a voice cried out for her, "Don't you wanna watch the movie?"

She turned her head away to answer, but I heard her loud and clear. "No, thanks. I prefer this Mexican to that one."

I felt my resolve waver. Who could stand against such prose as this?

Angie grabbed a slice and joined us.

I spoke to Bob, for it was his opinion I had come for.

"I have news. I have decided to go back to college."

Bob nodded, and she smiled. It was he who spoke. "That sounds great. Do you think you'll get in?"

"I got a call today."

"Ah." Bob was realizing that I was coming to him at the end of the thing, not the beginning.

"What did they say?"

"Well, it was the dean."

"The dean called you?"

"Yeah."

Angie interjected. "Is that normal?"

"I don't think so."

She continued. "What did he say?"

"I believe his exact words were, 'Why should I let you back in my school?'"

Bob chuckled. I smiled large. What else could I do?

"What'd you say?"

"I told him I didn't have an answer. I told him there was no reason for him to let me back into his school. And then he hung up." I took a long draught of milk.

Bob is a quiet dude. But he is wise. Three times in my life, he has asked the exact right question. A question that burned through all showmanship and ego. This was one of those times.

"What do you want him to do?"

The question stopped me. I had no charming answer. I was finally doing things again. I was jumping off the cliff to see if there was water underneath. I was beginning to hope again. The doing had plenty of rewards. But what did I really want? "I want them to take me back. I want to go back to Chicago and finish what I started. I want to finish my training, so that I might serve God and his church well."

There it was. After all the running, I was still a man under compulsion. I had a call on my life, and I wanted to honor that responsibility.

Bob smiled. "Now we know how to pray."

And we did pray. And one week later, a letter arrived telling me I had once again been accepted to the Moody Bible Institute.

It is an odd thing, seeing the shaping of your personhood summarized in a few paragraphs. Your love story condensed into a novella, maybe. But the epic journey that made you so much who you are, encapsulated into a chapter? Weird. Granted, this is a snapshot of who I was - or how I was perceived - at a moment (or a month) of time. It's still surreal. I feel like I ought to give backstory or caveats. But then I think, Ernesto does such a great job of painting the picture, maybe I'll just let it stand.

Maybe I'm just rendered speechless by the flattery of being likened unto Jane Eyre.

Mixed Tape

"Some are baffled, but that one is not - that one knows me."
   -Walt Whitman, in "Among the Multitude"

"The thing about Rivendell is... you can't stay there."
   -Ernesto at this farewell, as quoted in Angie's journal

I drive too fast. I drive to get where I'm going. The fields and the skies are wasted on me. They fade into white noise behind my purpose. I just want to get where I'm going. I want to pull into the driveway and be where I want to be.

But this day I drank it in. I drove the speed limit and took my time. There are stories on these long highways. Downtowns long forgotten. Fast food joints springing up on newly rediscovered exits. Factories with half-full parking lots holding on for one more year. I took it all in. This was my last drive to the farm. The van was packed with my college gear. It looked much different now than when I first drove to Chicago. I had so much stuff back then. Three suitcases of clothes. A hundred pounds of books. A dinosaur of a computer that introduced me to the world of Mac. This time there was no computer. There were no books. Just a duffel, a pillow and a blanket, all stuffed into an old laundry basket.

It was a foolish thing driving north to go south. I was adding two hours to an already five-hour drive. But the tree farm had become for me a sacred place. It was a place imbued with the love of a people. I'd never seen that before. I had loved people, and had intruded into their homes. But Hidden Hollows, the actual space, was designed and filled with the faith its makers carried.

Pulling in I was glad to see that they were home. My hands became instantly sweaty, and I hoped that she was home too. I may tell others that I came to say goodbye to Bob, but it was Angie who made me nervous. She was an incredible woman, and I longed to know her more. Alas, I was not yet a man worth loving. But sometimes it is just nice to be tempted.

Bob came outside to greet me. I jumped down from the still-running van. I actually hate goodbyes. I have learned over the years that they matter, so I forced myself to partake. I wanted to give Bob a hug, to tell him I loved him. But I didn't. Pride and machismo are a heck of a thing to break. I hugged Mrs. Kaye, because that was allowed. The screen door slammed a third time and out walked Angie, out into the blue of a completely clear sky.

"Hey, Nesto."

"Hey."

"You ready to go?"

"Yeah. The Beast is all packed."

I stood an awkward distance from her. It was not a cool amount of distance. No. I was overcompensating.

"I have something for you."

"Oh yeah?"

"Yeah." From my pocket I pulled a cassette. It was titled "For Angie."

I charged ahead. "The first side is songs I thought you might like." I paused, to let it sink in for a moment. "The B-side is my life story in song. In case you were wondering." I looked hard into her eyes. I wondered if she understood all I wasn't saying. That tape spoke without speaking. It said, "I know you, and I want you to know me."

The moment was over, so I landed the plane. "When I come back next year, maybe you'll have a tape for me."

She smiled. "Too late." And then, from her back pocket, she produced a cassette of her own. It was like a magic trick.

I reached out slowly to take it. My affection for her was strong. Words wanted to come forth. But it was not time. I had to go, and I had to go now.

I played it cool one last time. "I'm impressed."

"We'll see."

I looked down and saw the title of her tape. It was lovingly called, "Sounds of Freedom: anthems of a liberated woman."

"This should really win over my new roommate."

I smiled large, and then disengaged our connection. I turned to Bob and Kaye. "I got to get on the road. I got a long drive ahead of me, and I want to get some sleep before classes start tomorrow."

With that I jumped back into my van and was off. I waited until I cleared earshot and put on the tape. I was transfixed. I was so focused I didn't even notice the van begin to pull right. It was always a rough ride so I just ignored it. Then the whole car began to shake, so I pulled to the side of the road. The front driver-side tire had blown out. I was only five miles away from the tree farm. I could easily walk back to Bob for help. I looked down the road toward Hidden Hollows for quite some time. Finally I turned from it and began to walk the other way. I had already said goodbye to her once. I didn't have the strength to do it again. The summer was over, and so were we.

Oh, I knew what he was saying with that tape. Or at least some of it. I wrote in my journal about how special it was - how Side A being "songs she would like" ('High Fidelity' reference completely intended) "meant he went out on a limb." My reaction contained such expressions as "blown away" by how well he pegged me.

They're both still good mix tapes (now playlists) in their own right, but the risk he took, claiming to know me well enough (after taking time to actually do so, mind you; this wasn't a shot in the dark) to know what I'd like - what would speak to me, even - was pretty impressive. I smile every time I hear one of those songs.

PART TWO

SUMMER 2002

The Phone Call

"I am determined that only the deepest love will induce me into matrimony. So I shall end an old maid."
  -Elizabeth Bennett, in Jane Austen's *Pride and Prejudice*

Angie had just made peace with being single forever when Ernesto asked her to marry him.

Being single in church world does not wear well. It is a fashion that many well-meaning friends and family feel the need to remedy. There is the constant questions about some special someone. And everyone seems to know some eligible bachelor one town over.

Angie became more aware of this as years passed and she watched her college friends marry. She would serve, she would attend, she would even give a speech if asked. Never did she pity herself. Many women long for love and family. Angie had a different dream.

Her heroes were not Snow White or Aurora. These helpless girls spent their entire story waiting for someone to save them. No. Angie embraced two women whose lives changed the world. First, there was Aunt Esther. Aunt Esther was a missionary who had served the peoples of West Africa. She had ventured overseas and lived among the indigenous people for decades, before internet and cell phones shrunk the world. When she retired and came back to America, it was to her that Angie would look for inspiration. When Angie talked with her about how she wanted to follow in her aunt's footsteps, serving the poor and overlooked of the world, Aunt Esther cautioned her, "Oh, Angie. It will break your heart." Angie responded, "My heart is already broken; I might as well do something about it."

Then there was Mother Teresa. For many years, Angie had this crazy dream of traveling to Calcutta, becoming Mother's best friend, and then inheriting the vision of the Sisters of Charity. But then she had the opportunity to talk with someone who had known Mother Teresa and worked with her. The wise old man offered her some incredibly insightful counsel, stating that she needed to be faithful with what God had given her, not try to merely adopt someone else's calling. His words stuck with her: "Find your own Calcutta."

And so she had. She put down her tool belt and began to serve at her local church for a small monthly stipend. She couldn't afford it, but she knew making the gospel of Jesus known was the only thing worth giving her life to. So she plunged headlong into bringing teams into unreached areas across the globe. She led high schoolers into the mountains of Mexico. She traversed wildest Africa. And she was finally heading to the Himalayas.

In all of that traveling, she thought little of love or marriage. There had been suitors, but none that knew her. Some had thought her pretty, but that was not the point. Some had found her convenient, and that sounded awful. She wanted something else. So her suitors never really got her attention.

It was here that she prepared for Nepal. She was going to take a prayer trek through the Himalayas, seeing villages that had never seen a white woman. She was going to pray God's movement across two continents and test her mettle. And who knows, maybe God would open a door to Calcutta. She packed. She prepped. She was ready.

And then two planes sailed into the Twin Towers. That event changed the world more than many realize. With increased boldness, certain terrorist groups began making their presence known. Even in faraway Nepal, rebel insurgents threatened to take over the capital city. The organizers of her trek said it was very dangerous. They themselves didn't say she couldn't come, but they warned; everyone else in the group cancelled. Angie heeded the warning as well. It broke her heart to do so. To lay down yet one more dream to the cruelness of the world. She had faced doors closed due to inexperience, due to her gender, and now terrorism had claimed a small part of her heart.

That's why she was there when Ernesto came back.

Young men came and went on Hidden Hollows Tree Farm. Her father was a pied piper for lost young men trying to find their way. Many of these ragamuffins took notice of her, but she wore a sign defying anyone to try.

The summer had been nice, seeing him around the tree farm from time to time. He was kind. He was a bit of a mess. But it was an adorable mess. Like a monkey in a wedding.

The day after she had laid down Nepal, Ernesto had been there at the door once more. He had come from school with a car full of friends. She was surprised to find that she was happy to see him.

Month after month, the doorbell would ring. And there he would be. Sometimes alone. Sometimes with guests. Nearly always smiling.

Soon, there was added to his visits correspondence. He would write to her. At first he wrote her about that tape he made her when he left. Even when the songs ran out, he kept writing. He had this dumb rule; he would never send two emails in a row. He would send an email and let it hang in the world. He would not initiate contact again until she "hit the ball back to him." She tested this once, letting his message sit for two weeks. She realized if she wanted the emails to stop, she could just let the ball bounce into a ditch. As it were, she always hit it back. She really enjoyed those letters. He wrote like the Apostle Paul would if he had been a raging drunk. Emotions and words spilled across the page with seeming recklessness.

But it wasn't reckless. That was the really weird part. He swung away with everything, but never said anything about her. There was never an "us" or a "we." There was a "you" and "me." Any kind of talk about relationship seemed too much for this wordsmith to handle. She assumed this was because he was just passing the time. He had come for her father. Their friendship would end when that did. So talking was fun, but it was not meaningful. The thought made her sad. But it was okay. It was a great distraction.

She was sitting on the couch with a pencil in her hand when the phone rang. She put her journal down and walked to the phone. The phone seldom rang past eight, so she was curious as to who could be calling this night.

"Hello?" The voice on the phone was hesitant, but it was known. It was Ernesto, calling from faraway Chicago.

"Hey." She was curious, but not enough to reveal the card.

"Ang?"

"Yeah. It's Angie. You want me to go and get my dad?" It was the easiest answer as to why he would be calling this night.

"No, that's cool."

"Ok." And with that, she waited. Like most introverts, she didn't like phones. She liked writing much better. There was more time. And on top of that, the phone took away the personal from the conversation. If you couldn't see the face of the person you were talking to, how did you know what they were really saying?

"I wanted to talk to you about summer."

"Ok."

"Well, I know I asked for prayer about a job, and I wanted to let you know I found one. Terry offered me a job on the ranch all summer. It covers food, lodging, and pays enough for next year's tuition."

"That's great, Ernesto." She was genuinely happy for him, but she noticed a small disappointment within herself.

"Yeah, I think so. It really came out of nowhere, and it's gonna be perfect. I have another option, but I have concerns."

For the first time, she heard it. It was there in the words as he spoke. She heard the smile form. It had crept in during that last phrase. That concerned her as well.

Silence hung on the line. If he expected her to ask some question, then he hadn't been paying attention.

Finally he spoke.

"I could come back to Michigan. There is not much for me there. But I could work two full-time jobs and make as much as I would make in Dakota."

In her mind's eye, she saw him thinking. He was testing the water time and time again, and she was giving him nothing in return. She didn't want to be the factor for what he was going to say next. No, if he was gonna say this, he had to do it on his own.

"Honestly Angie, I am afraid to come home. 'Cause if come back to Michigan, I would not leave unscathed."

"Oh."

Ernesto cleared his throat. She could see him concentrating. He did that sometimes. He often spoke with a stutter, and would stop and plan out the words in order to get them to come out right. She could hear that slowness now.

"I like you, Angie. If I come home, I am going to be around you as much as I am able. And I am willing to pay for whatever that brings."

The words hung out there like the last line of your favorite song.

"I don't know what to say to that."

He laughed. Not at her. But because of her. She liked that.

"You don't need to. I am not asking you to make a decision for me. I am just telling you what I have been thinking. I thought maybe you might make this easy for me by telling me I'm just a good friend and you don't view me like that. Then I can head out west alone but not lonely. But don't worry about that. You get some rest. I'm gonna make a decision in the morning. And I'm sure you'll know my will soon enough. Have a good night, Ang."

"You too."

She hung up the phone.

Her mom, Kaye, walked into the kitchen. "Who was that?"

"It was Ernesto."

"Oh. How is he doing?"

"Fine. He's doing fine. I'm... gonna go to bed early tonight. I'll see you in the morning."

"Okay. Good night."

The thoughts were too many. They were too strong. She would sleep on it. Surely it would be clearer in the morning.

I remember this conversation a little differently. Still forward, to be sure, but not quite so direct. Maybe that's because at first I didn't know what it was leading up to. We talked about other things for awhile - movies, school, everyday life kind of stuff. But when we got down to the nitty-gritty, the lines I remember went something like, "If I came and spent the summer near you, I would not walk away unscathed. I'd wind up being crazy about you." Yah. He actually said that. Those were the words I couldn't get out of my head...

The Email

"This is all very foreign and new to me. No amount of Jane
Austen novels and Meg Ryan movies can prepare a thinking
girl for a fantastic guy to be crazy about her... What's a girl
to do in reality?"
    -Angie's journal, that week

The morning rose first in Michigan, and then over in
Chicago. Angie awoke earlier than normal and made her
way downstairs. She made her coffee the way she always did,
a light brown with much sweetness. She smiled looking at it.

She walked into the makeshift office and booted up the
large Gateway computer. It powered on, and she connected
via modem to her Juno email account. There were many
emails that needed attention. She scrolled right by them and
pushed the "New Message" button. She began to type.

"my first goal for the day is shot; though i slept well for a
couple hours, i can not sleep any longer. the house is quiet,
but my mind is not. so, since sleep evades me, you become
my first priority. this means that i've skipped several emails
from other people that come before yours in my inbox,
which is unusual for me to do. but i can see that i won't be
able to focus on anything else today until I express some of
what is swirling in my brain. I can also imagine that on such

58

a day as this, long though it is for you, you might wish for some word from me. it occurs to me that it might be a kindness to write promptly...

i know you didn't ask anything, but i still feel a more appropriate - or at least more complete - response is due than what has already been given. when the topic is cross-gender relationships, i can talk for hours... basically, i think i've got it all figured out. but when i speak assuredly of commitment and feelings and choices, it's all just "out there somewhere". when it comes back down to me as a person, as a woman, I find myself stripped of my eloquence and my clever constructs. sometimes a girl's just speechless. it certainly isn't that i have nothing to say; I just don't know how to say it. the irony is that there is more need than ever for clear communication and understanding... i feel i responded very poorly last night, but in truth i don't know what I could've said. witticisms and movie quotes fall short in such a situation... in fact, i'm still at a loss. it's not that i'm shocked or perplexed - though maybe slightly baffled.... i almost feel like i have to give you an entire history of my life in order to be understood. but that would take entirely too long and bore us both. suffice it to say that i don't know how to answer such admissions, because i have almost never in my life heard them. until only very recently, i had these impenetrable walls up, which no male would attempt to approach. everyone knew i was unattainable, and it'd be a waste of their time to try to break through the shell. this served me very well, because i was protected and independent. the problem was that it wasn't entirely true. though i truly am independent and quite comfortable with not needing a man, i've realized just in the last year or two that i spoke too strongly at times; and i've slowly started dismantling the armor. this is a hard task and a scary place for me, because suddenly i am open to a whole lot of things i never before had to consider. and suddenly people are free to speak to me of things they never would've broached before, because i wouldn't allow it. you didn't know me with all my shields, though much still remains. and i'm glad that the walls have fallen enough for you to see in. if you had come along much sooner, i may not have let you truly know me; i wasn't there yet. and your friendship means a great deal to me, so i do not lament having allowed so much. i just don't really know yet how to handle myself outside the fortress...

i must admit that i was not entirely surprised to hear that i am among the reasons you've decided to go away for the summer. the same thought had already crossed my mind. it seems arrogant to even say that, but i'm not a complete idiot; i know how things work. i knew it was neither impossible nor unlikely for such a possibility to be considered; you're a guy, i'm a girl, and we enjoy each other's company [a grossly simplistic summary, i know]. I wondered what might come of it too. so when you said you might not leave unscathed, i understood you immediately. and i could no longer argue, because i don't want there to be any scathing. and it becomes even more essential that I not try to sway you, that i stay far away from the methods of manipulation; i can not reason with you objectively, now that i know i am among the reasons. but i will tell you this anyway: my feeling, my preference is unchanged. i prefer having you near rather than far. but i understand and respect your consideration; i do not think it cowardly. it sounds a bit more like sensitivity and thoughtfulness to me...

i do not think you careless. I have been on the receiving end of careless words before, and this was something quite different. I think you kind and thoughtful. i appreciate your wanting to be "helpful" and not wanting to muddle my mind. you needn't worry about me. i appreciate honesty, and i think you should be free to say what you mean. i'll do my best to reciprocate.

i guess that's enough for now.

love,

ang."

She wrote all these things down. She read and re-read her words. They were true. Her coffee mug was on empty, so she rose and refilled it. She came back to the screen, having had a moment to reflect. The words still rang true. So she pressed "Send." The sound of a rushing wind came from the computer speakers. Off it went. Now all she had to do was wait for the ball to be hit back.

Ground Rules

"I don't need a man. I can say that without bitterness or spite or pride. I just believe that God has made me a complete person on my own and I can live a fully satisfied life entirely alone."

    -Angie to Ernesto, May 2002

    "Dude!"

It was Knuth who uttered the cry. Ernesto turned to see him staring at the jumper cables connecting his ghetto van to Terry's Bronco. They were standing in the parking lot at America's Roller Coast, Cedar Point. It was 10pm, and most of the cars were already gone. But the ghetto van needed a jump. Alas, Ernesto had crossed the streams. He had attached positive to negative and was about to witness the error of doing so.

The wrong connection didn't create an explosion, but instead created heat. The jumper cables had gotten so hot that the plastic surrounding them had begun to melt. Knuth, Ernesto, and the rest stared on as plastic ran off the cables like water over a cliff. Ernesto put out a hand to touch the red and black stream. It was a careless gesture, like putting your finger in a car lighter.

    "Ernesto! No!"

Ernesto pulled his hand back at the last second. He looked up at Knuth and realized he had almost been really hurt. He put his sweatshirt around his hands and pulled the pinchers off the van battery. The cables fell to the ground in a pool of red and black taffy. Around the circle stood a dozen staring faces. It was Knuth who spoke first.

"That was the craziest thing I have ever seen."

Ernesto looked around and saw a problem. He had arranged this trip to bring some of his college crew to the best roller coaster park on the planet. But that was just cover. He wanted to see Angie. It was only three weeks till he was home. But like the man said, when you know who you want to spend the rest of your life with, you want the rest of your life to start as soon as possible. So here they all met. The crew from Chicago and Angie from the north. They met here to walk and talk and ride and scream. It had been a good day.

Two cars had come full from Chicago. Only one remained. One car was heading back to the Windy City. The other was headed north with Angie at the wheel.

Ernesto spoke to the waiting crowd. "Okay, guys. Here is the plan. All the girls will go back in the Bronco with Terry. The guys, we are headed north to Angie's Tree Farm. I will get you back to school by Sunday night. Will that play?"

The Real Scott Johnson held up a hand. "I have to play violin at church in the morning."

"Well, Scott, looks like you are headed back in a car full of women."

He smiled. What college guy wouldn't?

"The rest of you guys are with me."

Ernesto looked at Angie. He had just invited a car full of guys to her home. He just volunteered a car ride home and a loaner to Chicago. He looked at her to see if she would flinch. Just how cool was this girl? She gave him the nod.

They drove three hours north to the Tree Farm, and the boys got to walk into the Last Homely House. It was like no place they had ever been. It was the first house they had ever visited that had a name. It takes a special kind of person to name their home, and an even better person to actually live up to it. The Simses called it Hidden Hollows. But the Chicago crew would call it Rivendell. They rolled in after midnight with no warning and the Elves got busy. Within the hour there was coffee, food, and the perfect lighting for meaningful conversation. Every one of the crew that entered would call it home in some way. This place was an island of peace.

It was a late night in the great room. The five from Chicago, Angie and her sister Wendi, Ma and Pa Sims, all gathered together to talk too loud and laugh too freely. One by one people began to drop off. Soon, all had gone to bed or fallen asleep right there on the shag carpet. Only two remained. A man and the woman he longed to marry.

Angie spoke in a whisper. And not just for those who slept at their feet. "What do you tell your friends about me?"

"What do you mean?"

"What word do you use to describe me?"

"What are you asking me?"

"How do you describe the nature of our relationship?"

"Oh." His smile became a smirk. "I simply tell them that I'm your man and you are the only girl for me."

Ernesto and Angie both enjoyed prose. Angie wielded it on the page with beauty and authority. But she was not accustomed to speaking that language in the world of people and things. This was a language she spoke in private, in journals and in prayer. This man before her spoke the same language. But he spoke it out loud with the boldness of a poet's pen. He looked her in the eye and shot the arrow true and clean. It left her flustered. He found that just wonderful.

"Just say what you need to say, Ang."

She spoke kindly but strongly. "I don't know if I want to be your girl."

"I know."

"You say that now. But what are you gonna say at the end of the summer? What if I don't know what to do with you by the time you go back to school?"

"Well then, I guess I'll chase you from afar."

"For how long?"

"That's a good question." He leaned back in his chair and closed his eyes. He thought through the question honestly. "Until May 10th of next year."

"Wow. That's a very specific date."

"It's my graduation day. Look, Angie. You are an incredible woman. I have come back to Michigan asking for you to give me your heart. I am all in. But not indefinitely. When I graduate college, if you don't know your will concerning me, then I will just leave. I'll head off to the mission field a single man, and I will mourn the loss."

"So you're giving me an ultimatum."

"Geez. That's a pretty sharp point to put on it. But sure. If you want to call it that, then sure. If you don't know your heart concerning me within a year of life, I'm going to walk away."

She sighed. "Look, I had let go of the idea of ever being married. I was content serving the Lord as a single woman all the days of my life. You were not part of my reckoning. If I'm going to do this, I have to be sure. I don't want to give you any false hope. So until I have made up my mind, I can't give you anything. No promises. No affection. No hope.

Because if I decide I don't want to be your girl, I don't want to answer to God for taking things that weren't mine."

"You've promised me nothing. You've given me no hope. Your hands are clean."

She nodded.

"And knowing all that, here I am. I will be at your door as often as I'm able. And it is my great dream that you would give your love to me."

With that, he got up. "It's getting late. I will see you in the morning." He left the room and her presence. He was aware that behind him, she did not move. She just sat near the window staring out into the night. He hoped that was a good sign.

The boys woke up late. Real late. The Sims clan gave them the Lumina knowing that Ernesto would be back. Laughter and chaos ensued as all the guys said their goodbyes. The car was loaded; the doors were closed. Ernesto got into the driver seat and inserted the key. The Simses stood outside to wave goodbye. It was a very polite gesture. Bob, Kaye, Angie, and Wendi stood there waiting to give their farewell.

There was one problem. The key wouldn't turn. It would not rotate. Ernesto felt the embarrassment rising. He took the key out and put it back in. Nothing. He tried to wrench on the steering wheel to free the tires. Nothing. The guys weren't noticing yet. They were too busy getting situated. Knuth was riding shotgun and seeing what mixtapes he had for the ride home. Sweat begin to gather on the back of Ernesto's neck. He hated this kind of thing. He didn't like looking foolish.

"What's going on, Ern?" Knuth spoke with a hint of venom.

"This key won't turn."

The guys in the backseat were watching. They began to give advice. "Is the car in Park?" "Is the wheel locked?" "Are you sure you have the right key?" And still nothing.

From the farewell party, Wendi came forward. She was the youngest of the sisters, and at least two of the guys had taken notice of her during this adventure. She walked over to the window and leaned in. "What's up?"

Ernesto spoke as a man defeated. "I can't get the car to start." He sat with his hands to his side. He was tired. He was embarrassed. And he felt downright stupid.

Wendi real casual-like reached an arm in, took the key, and with a gentle touch turned it fully. The engine roared to life. Still leaning there in the window, she smiled the smile of a knowing girl and said, "You're trying too hard."

She stood up, and walked back to the sidewalk.

The boys sat in silence. Ernesto put the car into drive, and began to roll away. Ernesto could hear the snickers in the back. He dared not look over at Angie. When they cleared the driveway the car exploded into laughter.

The double entendre had struck. Wendi spoke about the car. But she also spoke to the man who was pursuing her sister. And she had just gutted him before this romance had even started.

Even as the boys chattered in the back, Knuth spoke from the passenger seat. "Man, make sure you don't get your hopes up on this one. You might be aiming a little high."

The laughter only strengthened Ernesto's resolve. He spoke not to Chris, but aloud to himself. "It is not her love that is my hope. My hope is that the love exists. And I will love her. I will love her."

A History of Women

"The love of God is the gospel I preach, but the hardest thing in the world to accept."
    -Ernesto Alaniz

"Every chance we get to show someone what unfailing love would do brings a little more beauty into this messed up world."
    -Angie to Ernesto, in an email

"Angie, I want you to know the worst there is to know about me so that you are able to make an informed decision."

Angie just stared at him. This is not where she saw this going at all.

They sat in his mother's basement, sitting on a couch that had once ruled the seventies. The bare walls were a lifeless grey, and the rafters were full of all manner of cobwebs.

"I have dated a grand total of five girls in my life. Only two of them really matter to our conversation. One of them I gave my body, the other my heart."

Ernesto was visibly shaken. But he kept on.

"You can know whatever you want."

"The girl of your heart. Does she have any hold over you?"

He smiled. "No. I can say that with total and complete confidence."

"How is that possible?"

"Angie, the day after I declared my intentions to you, she came back for me. She reached out to rekindle a long dead romance. And I rejected the advance. I have been tempted and found faithful. I am your man, and you are the only girl for me."

She wished that could end the conversation. But there was more to be said before the day was over.

"Okay. You say you gave this woman your body. Does that mean… you are no longer a virgin?"

This was something that she had known would come up. She didn't know it would be so soon, but she knew that someday they would talk about sex. She had always wondered how much it would matter. She had always known she would care if her future husband had been sexually promiscuous, but how much of an effect would it have if he had not waited for her the way she waited for him? And right then she knew the answer. It did matter to her. She wasn't looking for someone to walk through life with. But, if she were to give her heart to some man, she wanted that man to be fully and wholly hers. She braced for his answer.

"Angie, I have never laid with a woman the way a husband lies with his wife."

She felt tears. She hated that. She had all the will in the world, but she couldn't control her own emotional reactions.

"I am a virgin, but I am not without sin. I have been more intimate than I ever intended." And then he spoke. He shared the what. It was not salacious, but it was defined.

He looked down the whole time he spoke. He did not speak long, but it was long enough. She rose from the couch.

"I am gonna head back to the tree farm."

He didn't rise or raise his head.

"I know."

And with that she walked up the stairs, through an empty house she had never seen full of people, and began the drive back north to safety.

In the privacy of her car she could let the tears fall. She laughed at herself for being so silly, and the tears started up once again. They were not bitter tears. They were the tears that came from accepting a hard thing. He had been up front with her about all things. For that, she was grateful.

She believed God's way was the best way. God had spoken about the beauty and power of human sexuality. But He had given it a context. Sexual union was reserved for a man and woman under the covenant of marriage. That's the teaching of Christ, of Yahweh, of the Church. She had always known that. She had seen the consequences of the other life. She watched kids born with absent fathers. She had seen shotgun weddings and the awful aftermath of such a thing. It was always her will to wait. She had even done one of those purity pledges in junior high. Sure, it was a little cheesy. But it had been deadly serious for her. She had made a promise to God and kept it. And if she were going to make another promise, a death-do-us-part promise, then she wanted it to be God's way. She wanted someone who had waited for her the way she waited for him.

She knew his history and had only two choices. She could forgive a young man for his mistakes, or hold it against him and get out while the getting was good. The thought of leaving was only briefly considered. Yes, this knowledge would bring hurt and insecurity later. But she was willing to endure that. And she knew what forgiveness actually meant. It meant not dwelling on this. It meant not holding his past against him. By the time she made it to the tree farm, she was at peace. He was forgiven. She would give him the chance.

She came back the next day to see him. When she pulled up he was on the porch waiting for her. He was smiling. It was a good smile, and she was growing quite fond of it. It reminded her of the Cheshire Cat from *Alice in Wonderland*.

"It's good to see you."

"It's good to see you, too."

This was how it was for a bit. Polite. Kind. A restrained boldness giving her the space she needed.

They once again went into the dungeon of a basement that he called a room.

"You forgive me?"

"I forgive you."

"I am glad."

"So, what's next?"

"Well, I guess there are the compatibility questions. To make sure we want the same things out of life."

"Whatcha got?"

"First question. Is there any mental health issues in the women in your family?"

"What?"

"Are any of the women in your family crazy?"

She laughed. "What kind of question is that?"

"It's a completely fair question. They say crazy genes are hereditary. So, if you got crazy in your blood, I want to know it. Look... an old man I know lost his life by marrying a crazy woman. He was faithful to her care his entire life. But he told me to make sure I knew what I was getting into. I don't want you to steal my life from me."

"That is a really awful question."

"Awful as you may call it, the question stands."

"No. None of the women in my family have had psychotic breaks."

"Sweetness. Next question."

"Hold on. I think I get a turn."

"Oh, by all means. Fire away."

"Are you willing to go anywhere and do anything that God might call us to? Including the farthest mission field?"

"Angie, I have every intention of getting to the mission field as soon as possible. My life belongs to God's kingdom, and there is nothing I won't give for its advancement."

"Acceptable."

"Nice. How many children do you want to have?"

"None."

And just like that, all the air went out of the room.

"What do you mean, none?"

"I don't want any kids."

"I don't understand."

Ang slowed down her speech to emphasize the point. "I don't want to have any children."

"But Angie... that's kind of the point of marriage."

She did not like where this was going.

"God gave Adam and Eve marriage, and told them to be fruitful and multiply. That is like the second command given to humanity. To make babies."

"What about those couples who are unable to have kids?"

"Well, then they have to mourn that loss. But for those who are able, we are called to do it. And not only that, but babies are a blessing. Why would you not want a blessing?"

"Listen, I never intended to get married. And so I have never considered being a mother. It's not on my radar."

Ernesto slumped back into the old couch. "Ang, I have dreamed of being a father my entire life."

"Then you have to ask yourself a question. Do you still wish to give your love to me knowing what you know?"

He looked off to the upper right of his vision, the place he always looked when digging through the wreckage. The past was in there, unspoken but ever moving. He had never known a father. His own had been out of the picture since he was but a boy. The only memory he had was his shadow. Mother and father were putting him to bed. He couldn't see his face, but it was him. He was saying good night. And that was it. A faceless father who had never come back. When he was young, he used to get presents from this man on his birthday. It was only much later that he realized his mom was just putting a ghost's name on gifts she herself had bought. Many boyfriends and stepfathers had come through their front door. But none of them ever wanted to pat his head and say good job.

All this lack had become a desire. He would do it right. He would raise up a child and not leave. He would say the words and give the hugs. He would put them to bed and keep them safe from the bad men outside. It never occurred to him that she wouldn't want this very same thing.

He looked back at her. She had asked him a question, and he was going to have to answer it. Was he still in? He thought about all he had said in the last few years. He talked about love as commitment. It was a promise made not to the beloved, not found in the object being loved. No. Love was found within the lover. The God of heaven doesn't love a soul because it is beautiful. His love cannot be earned and therefore cannot be lost. It is within Himself. He chooses to love. That decision is why Christ was given. That unchanging and unflinching choice brings freedom for all those who would receive the free gift of God's grace.

Ernesto had learned all these things. He lived in the freedom of God's good love. He wanted to love like God loved. That meant the promise was given, and the flaws were seen, and the love still given.

After five minutes of silence, five minutes of waiting, Ernesto spoke.

"I still want to pursue you. I am your man, and you are the only girl for me."

He leaned forward to be nearer to her. "But, I want you to know something. If you give your love to me, and we walk down that aisle together, I am gonna spend the rest of my life praying against your stance. I am going to pray that God gives you a desire for children, and if not that, then I will ask God to break any prevention methods currently in existence."

"Well, I suppose I can allow that." There was a smile on her face. But the smile had some concern.

"What are you thinking?"

"Your whole life? Really?"

"Really."

"Is it because you never had a father?"

"Yeah."

Now she had to make a choice. She could choose to speak or to be quiet. But if she were silent now, it would be the end.

"Ernesto, you have to let me see where you came from. It keeps coming up. Your life before college. You say it doesn't matter, but it obviously does. It is why you want kids so bad. I don't need all of it. But it can't be off-limits to me."

"What does that look like?

"Well, I guess I wanna know how you grew up. And I want to meet your family. I have been over to this house three times now, and I have never met your parents or your brothers."

He stood up. "Let's go. The movie starts in 30 minutes."

She stood up with him. But she was not going to let this go. "And?"

"And, I'll let you see where I come from."

"Thank you."

"If this is gonna be a real thing, then you need to know what you're signing up for." He scratched his arm absently. "But this stuff is hard for me. Just so you know."

"I know."

The two walked up the stairs and into the world.

Flint

"We might be through with the past, but the past ain't
through with us."
   -Jimmy Gator, *Magnolia*

Love stories are never just two people. There are ghosts
following close behind. Family, broken hearts from years
past, and even the current tribe of coworkers are all pulled
along. You are not loving this one person, but all that is
attached to them. Ernesto knew those Angie loved the most.
He knew her parents, her sisters, and even a few cousins. He
had walked among the very trees that Angie climbed on as a
little girl. But Ernesto was an island, or at least there was a
part of him that was closed off. The spirits of his past
remained far away.

Or they had until this day.

The whole drive had been in silence. But he began to
speak as they drove east into the city.

"This road is the dividing line between the haves and
have-nots. On one side are U. of M., Mott Community
College, and the entire cultural district of the city. But the
other side of this road has been left to itself." He hit the
blinker and made the left, taking them from the haves and
pushing into the have-nots.

"The Flint you know is back that way. This is the Flint I know. This is the State Streets."

Angie had never crossed this road before. He was right about that. She had come to this city to see plays, to go to the museums, to attend festivals. And she had always felt safe. She didn't know there was an unseen wall providing that safety.

She felt the weight in the car. Generally, he would be narrating the entire drive. It was his way of providing structure, a semblance of control. He would talk facts and figures, telling about who did what where. But his observations were few and far between.

"We're crossing Davison Road. You'll notice the neighborhood drops as you cross the intersection."

She did notice. The stoplights marked a descent. The houses were in worse shape. More and more were abandoned.

They came to another light, and he paused. The light was green, but the car just sat there running as though waiting on the red. No cars honked, for there was no traffic to be inconvenienced. Finally, he turned right.

"This is Leith Street. This was the good times."

As they drove East the neighborhood began to improve. They crossed Dort Highway and came into a nice stretch of road. Every house was occupied. The yards were mowed and free from clutter. At the end of Leith, they took a left onto Center Road. He pulled onto the shoulder and looked out the window at a newly constructed charter school. She waited. She knew that he had not been back to this place for many years.

"This was my grandma's house. It was right there."

His eyes stared at the green field that would soon know the sound of children playing. Once upon a time there had been a garage there. And a grove of pear trees that gave fruit to the entire family. And an above-ground pool. And a long winding driveway where the man who was never his grandfather had taught him to ride a bike. And the side yard where Tony had dropped the sparkler into his shoe. How he screamed as that carbon burned through shoe and flesh alike. It was all gone.

"We used to be able to walk over to the grocery store and buy candy bars." He spoke flat. He didn't want to reveal just how much this shook him.

He put the car into drive and performed an illegal u-turn. They headed back down Leith, and a few blocks down he stopped in the middle of the street.

"You see that eagle on that house?"

She looked out her window and saw a nice white home. Above the front door was a black tin eagle.

"That was the best house I ever lived in."

She turned to him. "Why was it the best?"

He smiled. She was gonna pull on him after all. He had wondered if she was gonna let him get through this without dealing with anything.

"It was just us. Me and the brothers and mom. It was only a year. But I remember being happy. I remember not being scared."

As he craned his neck to look up at the crest, she studied his face. She could see some joy there. But there were clouds as well. That house had been the eye of a storm. Peace had come, but it was only for a moment.

He continued back the way they came, until they came to the worst of the blight. He didn't turn back towards civilization. Instead, he steered the car deeper in. Angie noticed that very few houses seemed lived in. Some were eaten by fire. Some covered in graffiti. Others just left to the elements, overgrown with broken windows and wide open doors. Finally he pulled next to a curb, parked the car, and got out.

She followed. She stood next to him before an empty plot of land. It was overgrown with brush and had become a dumping pile for local garbage. She could hear the Flint River running just over the hill. And beyond that the expressway. She looked down the road and counted maybe four occupied houses. And even those were in increasing levels of disrepair.

Ernesto was void of emotion as he spoke. "My house used to be here. It was right here."

"What happened to it?"

"I don't know."

He walked up to the where the porch used to be and looked up those forgotten steps to his old front door. He remembered.

He was a boy. He and Tony and Jessie were all home alone. Mom was at work. She had gotten a new job as a pharmacist somewhere in the city. After she finished school there had been hope.

Jessie was listening to music in their room. Tony was in the shower. Ernesto was sitting alone in the living room watching the little tube TV. There was a knock on the door. He had answered it without thinking. He was a sweet boy and was slow in learning that monsters lurked behind every corner.

His attention was still on the television as he swung open the door. When he turned to see who it was, he stopped cold. They had been in hiding for over a year. Uncle and Grandfather had descended on their home like superheroes, and they had been rescued. His little boy self had assumed the nightmare was over.

Standing in the doorway was the man they had run from. As big as the whole world. Fear filled him then, and he would never feel safe again.

Ernesto stood before the empty parcel, and the memories flooded back.

"Ernesto?"

He shook awake. "Let's get out of here."

As they drove out of the desolation, he spoke.

"Angie. This is where I come from. You wanted to see it. You have seen it. But I don't want to talk about this stuff. There is nothing good that can come from it."

"You're wrong."

He grimaced. Her words challenged his own, and she had the higher ground.

"Angie. I don't want to talk about this stuff."

She considered this for a moment. She could see this was a red flag. A man who does not face his demons is ruled by them. This man beside her had built a new life after Christ. She could see that it was a real life. But it was incomplete. The grace of God had not touched the whole. It's like he pushed reset when he met Jesus and had been pretending that his whole life began at that moment. It was a romantic sentiment, but not how life works. We can't just erase the parts of the story we don't like. No. Jonah the prophet was a racist who never got over his prejudice. David the great king murdered for lust. We can't hide from the parts of the story we don't like.

"Okay."

She saw it. She knew it would bring them trouble. But she chose to walk with him anyway. She was not blind. But she was gracious.

So they drove out of that city. They headed south, to the house that wasn't a home.

Waterford

"All happy families are alike; each unhappy family is unhappy in its own way."
-Leo Tolstoy, *Anna Karenina*

As the great cities of America drifted toward crime, those with resources left the once splendored downtowns for a cookie cutter dream. Sprawling subdivisions seemed intentionally complex in their layouts, telling visitors they were neither wanted nor welcome. Sadly, the lines between suburbs and city were not just drawn on lines of class. They were also drawn on lines of color.

Waterford was near no expressway, had nothing to draw tourists, and was jokingly called "Water-tucky" by those who lived in the surrounding communities. The name wasn't too far off the mark. On any given day you could find a Confederate flag flying off the back of a raised pick-up truck. But mixed in with the hillbilly culture was money. The town was full of lakes. There was not a straight street in the whole township. Every street had to wind its way through the many bodies of water which lent the area its name. The many lakes kept property values high and gave the lower middle class the opportunity to walk among giants.

On the edge of this quaint little burg was the dying city of Pontiac. Like the rest of the I-75 corridor, this city had once been a thriving metropolis, built on the back of the automotive industry. But as the car makers headed for cheaper labor many northern industrial cities were left in ruin. Flint, Pontiac, Saginaw, and Detroit were all broken cities with depressed populations and a decreasing tax base.

Ernesto's family lived one block from the train tracks. But they were on the right side of that line. That one block meant Waterford schools, Waterford police, and access to the movers and the shakers. It was a chance to stand up.

"So, you got everybody's name down?"

"Yeah. Maria and Mike are your parents. Antonio has glasses, and is the middle brother. Jesus is the baby and has long Messiah hair."

"And remember. My family is loud. They are not yelling. They are just talking. It's a Mexican thing. But if Mike starts yelling, that is actually yelling. If that happens, just follow my lead."

"What was it like moving from Flint to Waterford?"

He laughed. "It was... comical."

"Go on."

"Ang, I was not a cool kid in Flint. I was kind of a loser. But no one here knew that. So, I tried to come off like I was some inner city tough guy who was gonna take over the school. The cool kids didn't really like that."

"So what happened?"

"Okay. Up here on the right is my old middle school." He slowed the car down so she could see the old building. "I only went there for a minute, but that's all I needed. I got jumped my first week there. But it was a suburb beating, not a city one. They pushed me around, spit on me, smacked me a few times. But they didn't stomp my life into oblivion. Actually, that beating was the first time I ever prayed."

"Really?"

"Yeah. I had given my backpack and new coat to Tony, and told him to go home. I didn't want him to see his big brother catch a beating. So he left. And I took the hits. It was actually kinda crazy. They were swinging and pushing and laughing, and finally one of their girlfriends screamed for them to stop. She said something like, 'He isn't gonna run, and he isn't gonna fall. You've proved your point. Let him go.' And they let me go."

"Wow."

"I know. Pretty cool girl. I don't remember her name... Anyways. I came home pretty beat up, and Tony wasn't there. My backpack was, but he wasn't. And I had a horrible thought. What if he came out to find me? What if he ran into the crew that had just smacked me around? So I took off running back towards the very guys who had just put me down like a dog. And as I ran, I prayed. I asked God to save my little brother. And if he did, I would go to church. It was a weird thing. I don't know why I thought of church as so magical. I guess 'cause of all those horror movies. Monsters can never go onto holy ground. So I always viewed it as magical. But, that was the deal. Save my brother, and I will go to church."

"What happened to Antonio?"

"That fool had just gone to a buddy's house. But that didn't stop me from marching right up to the crew of boys that had just smoked me and asking them where my brother was. They laughed. But this one kid, the leader of the pack, he said they hadn't seen my brother. I believed him. Something about how he said it. As I was walking away he called out to me. 'Hey. No hard feelings man.' They had put me in my place. I had taken my beating well. And they never messed with me again."

"Did you go to church?"

"Not for another 6 months. And I didn't go because of that promise. I went because Tony went. He was my only friend. At church, we were split into different grades, so I couldn't be with Tony anyways. But the people I met there, they embraced me. They loved me when I was unlovable. I met Jesus there in that place."

"You and Tony still close?"

"Not as close as we once were." Ernesto made his thinking face, and sadness was found there. "But I can't wait to see him. I love him very much. And I miss him."

The van pulled off onto the shoulder in front of their family home. It was a nice home, on a nice street, in a nice little neighborhood. It was easy to see how a family could be raised here. 3 bedrooms. A basement. A nice yard. But today the house wasn't a home. Today the house was a disaster.

Ernesto came around the van and stared in horror at his mother's home. Strewn across the front yard were beer cans of every brand and size. A stray undergarment hung lifeless from a tree branch. Red solo cups lined the rails of the front porch. The front door was wide open.

Angie came up beside Nesto and surveyed the wreckage. "What's going on?"

He spoke. Not in answer to her question, but just needed to say the words aloud. "I'm gonna kill 'em."

They walked up the porch to the screen. Ernesto spoke. "Tony? Jesus?"

Nothing.

"Stay here."

He opened the screen and stepped in. The linoleum was sticky with dried beer. Every step made a tearing sound. He ventured down the main hallway, not knowing what he would find. He turned right towards the bedrooms and entered the bathroom. A keg lay in the bathtub, and he could see right away that the metal keg had scarred the porcelain tub. There was gonna be no hiding that. He then went to Tony's door and knocked. "Tony?" His tone was not a whisper. It was an angry older brother voice.

"Tony!"

He grabbed the door and pushed it open. And there on his bed in a drunken heap was the second musketeer, Antonio Moreno. He shook him. He shook him again. Some movement. He smacked him in the face.

"What, man?"

"Tony. It's Nesto. Where's mom?"

"She's gone, man. Her and Mike are on vacation."

"Where?"

"I don't know."

"Did they go by plane or car?"

"Plane." Tony was coming off an impressive bender, and he was slow to speak his answers.

"When do they get back?"

"I don't know man. What day is it?"

"It's Saturday."

"Well, then, they come home tomorrow."

Ernesto put his hand to temple and began to rub it. "Tony, the house is in shambles. They are gonna kill you."

Tony looked up at his older brother and they locked eyes. Ernesto hoped he heard him.

"I gotta throw up." He threw his blankets aside and ran to the bathroom.

Ernesto went back outside to find Angie sitting on the old iron and wood bench. He sat beside her.

"Whelp, this is Tony's doing alright. And mom is coming home tomorrow. So, he is screwed."

"What can I do to help?"

Ernesto looked over at her. She wasn't just saying that. She felt the weight of this small disaster, and wanted to offer her assistance.

"Angie. If they come home tomorrow and find the house this way, it's not gonna fall on Tony. It's gonna fall on my mom." She heard what he didn't say and nodded.

"Will you really help?"

"Yes."

He looked at her and felt the love in his heart grow for her. She was a truly kind woman. And not even this self-inflicted wound brought her disdain.

Antonio stepped out onto the porch and into a beautiful Michigan morning.

"Well, that was awful."

Ernesto stood. "Tony, you're an idiot." They laughed, and embraced. They were almost twins. But Tony was more athletic. Where Nesto had chosen books and study, Tony had run and played. And you could see it in their bodies. The frames were the same, but what they hung on it was very different.

"Tony, this is Angie, the girl I told you about."

She was already standing and put out a hand. He batted it away and went for the hug.

"Great to meet you. Ernie tells me you are the best."

She let herself be hugged. She didn't know it, but Tony has long been considered the best hugger in three counties.

"Well, he says the same about you."

"Not after today he won't."

"Here's the plan, Tony. We got 24 hours to get this house back into shape. I'm gonna head up to Meijer and get cleaning supplies. You and Angie start picking up cans and bagging all the trash. Angie will make up a list of what needs to be done. I gotta work in a few hours, so you two will stay here and make this place spotless."

"Great plan. But I got to head over to Steve's first. I put some of the pictures in Steve's car so they wouldn't get hurt during the party. I got to go get all that stuff. Then I will come back and help."

"Done. And, you are gonna give Angie some money for cleaning up after your dumb self."

"Dude. I wouldn't do her wrong like that."

"I'm just making sure."

Tony went in to get ready to go. Nesto turned to Angie. "Ang, I am gonna go and get supplies. Can you get started here?"

"I got this."

"Thank you, Angie."

With the brothers gone, Angie began to bag bottle returns and trash. She started outside and then made her way in. She finished the first floor and then headed downstairs. She had been down there before talking to Nesto, and was not surprised to find it in better shape than upstairs. It was a scary basement, even for a party. There were a few plates, a few bottles, and a spot. She saw it over near the western wall. She approached it. It was a pool of a thick red liquid. She stared down at it with great distrust. What was that?

A voice answered her unspoken question.

"It's blood."

She turned to see someone rising from Ernesto's couch-bed. He was a thin Mexican with an almost Jewish nose. His hair was long and straight, hanging over his eyes and reaching down to his shoulders. He looked like a heavy metal hero. He looked like a ganja hippie. He looked like -.

"Jesus."

"Yeah. Who are you?"

87

"I'm Angie. I'm… with Nesto."

"Oh. Ok."

He spoke not as someone fighting a hangover. He spoke like someone who has just been found floating on a piece of flotsam for six months. He spoke like someone who has forgotten how to speak. He spoke like someone who hasn't seen another soul in ages.

"Are you okay?"

"Do you believe in aliens?"

"Excuse me?"

"Aliens have chosen me. They speak to me. They are inside of me and talk to me. I don't know what they want with me."

Angie stood staring at him. He was clothed in shadow, and his soft voice was made horrible by the insane things he said.

He got up and stretched. He looked over at her. His glassy eyes looked to her and then to the floor. "It was a bloody nose. It was a real gusher." And with that he ambled upstairs. She listened and heard the bathroom door close. The toilet flushed and then the shower turned on. She went up the stairs and rushed outside.

She was waiting by the street when Ernesto returned. She told him all that had happened. Her fear went away quickly as she watched his response. She expected surprise, or even anger. But his response was a great and heavy sadness.

"Have you ever heard of huffing?"

"Huffing?"

"You spray an aerosol can into a brown paper bag. And then you breathe in those fumes with great intensity. It gives the user quite the high. It also kills brain cells and brings people to hallucinations."

"Your brother…."

He nodded. "He's a sweet boy, Angie. He is. He's just…
lost."

She looked at him and looked back to the house. With the
yard cleared, it looked like a very nice house. It looked like a
home. It really did.

The Curse

"Kindness falls like rain; it washes her away.
And Anna begins to change her mind."
-Counting Crows, "Anna Begins"

Ernesto was as good as his word. Whenever he had time he came to her door. But the time he had was very limited. He worked two full-time jobs as he tried to raise enough money to pay for his senior year of college. In the daytime he worked cleaning carpets down in Detroit. In the evening he would pick up shifts at Aldo's Carry Out, either cooking or delivering pizza or doing dishes. When you need the hours, no job is too low.

His schedule was such that he was only coming to her once a week. As summer wore on she took it on herself to come to him when he had an opening. She may not know what she wanted for the future, but she was up for the journey.

It was July, and summer was in full force. Their romance was very soon coming to a point of decision. Her questions were being answered. Time and presence brought wisdom. All that was left was the choosing.

Angie was prone to migraine headaches. It is a girl thing, tied to biological cycles that weren't going away anytime soon. But this one was a really bad one. The pain brought on by the uber-headache was such that nausea and incapacitation followed. She laid in her room with curtains drawn and door closed. She suffered alone.

She fell in and out of sleep as the day progressed. Sleep was good. Sleep made the pain go away. It waited for her whenever she awoke, but those reprieves were much welcomed.

As she lay there in her childhood room, she thought of Nesto's previous visit. He had come as he always did. Aloof but with great intention. As the night progressed, father and mother excused themselves and went to bed. Soon they found themselves alone in the great room. And unlike other late nights, they found themselves sitting on the same couch. It was funny how he always sat apart from her. At first she didn't notice. But as weeks turned to months she realized that he intentionally positioned himself far from her.

This night they sat on the same couch. After a bit there came a break in the conversation. The current topic had run out of steam, and another was not queued up directly behind it. It was into one of these lulls that Ernesto spoke.

"Angie?"

"Yeah."

"Can I hold your hand?"

Of course he asked. He was a gentleman in all things when it came to her. It was a beautiful night. The moon shone liberally outside, bringing a brightness into the dimly lit great room. Bathed in that light, sitting near his beloved, how could he not desire to touch her?

And she had wanted to say yes. To take his hand and hold it firmly. To gently stroke his thumb with her own. To feel that connection beyond friendship and into something more. But she had drawn a line in her heart. There was to be no physical affection until the promise was given. Until she had given her heart to this man, she would not enjoy his touch. And he would not know hers. To open that door would be to open a great dam, and she was wise enough to know how easy it was to drown therein. That was the choice she had made under the risen sun. And it was being challenged under the bright of the moon. She appreciated his asking. She wanted to share the moment. But it wasn't tonight. It wasn't now.

So she spoke. Kindly, but with authority. "No."

The word hung out there in the darkness like a slap. After a minute, Ernesto stood to rise. "I am gonna head back."

She listened as the door closed softly behind him. She could hear the big van roar to life, and she tuned into its engine until it had gone beyond the reach of sound.

Lying in bed with a headache, she smiled at the memory of it. He had been embarrassed. It was dumb, but she found it sweet. She was still smiling when there was a knock on her bedroom door.

"Hello?"

The voice that answered was not who she expected. It was not her mother's voice that answered. It was Ernesto's. "Ang, it's me. Can I come in?"

She had not showered that day. A bucket was by her head in case she threw up. A package of opened saltines balanced on its rim. Her hair was matted to her face like only a good fever can do. But here he was.

"Yeah."

The door opened, and he slowly came in.

"I called earlier, and your mom told me you were feeling bad." He stood there near the doorway. She looked miserable. "Anyways, I brought you some things to help you feel better. I got you some Diet Coke, 'cause that always settles your stomach." He reached into a plastic bag and pulled out a cold 20 oz bottle and placed it near her bucket.

"I got you some chocolate for when you can finally hold food down." She heard him fumbling around until he produced a bag of Hershey's Hugs - because Kisses would have been too much.

"And I got you one more thing." He turned from her and she heard him ripping something open. It gave him a little bit of trouble, but she finally heard the thing pop open. She heard the fuzz from a waiting CD and the whirring of the disc as it began to turn. Then the room filled with a soft guitar. She knew the song immediately. It was from her favorite movie of all time, *La Vita e Bella*, or *Life is Beautiful*. It was the greatest love story she had ever seen. Its theme came from her boombox, filling the room with great affection.

"I hope this helps. I will talk to you again soon." And with that, he backed out of her room, closing the door more gently than a man of his size seemed capable.

The guitar softly plucked away, and she felt the walls of her heart shake. For a while she didn't know what to do with this loud-mouthed stranger who had adopted her home as his own. Was he a man worth loving? Was he a man she would trust to lead their life together? She had seen his past and his present. She watched him as he counseled, preached, taught, and listened. She had watched the way he loved others, both the strong and the weak. Initially, the question was whether she could love this man. Then the question was, "Should I love this man?" She realized it now, the answer to both were yes. She cared for this man.

But it was too soon to say so. Maybe her girlish heart was betraying her. She had to be sure. She didn't want to speak before she was fully settled in her will. Her emotions were threatening to run away from her, and she would not be led by those fickle things. The music played and she was awed by the thoughtfulness of the gift. He had driven ninety miles one way to bring it to her.

The migraine persisted. The night was long. But in that moment Angie entered into an altogether different curse. When Adam and Eve disobeyed the living God, He punished them both. To Adam was given futility and work. To Eve was given pain in childbirth and something much less talked about. Everyone knows that having a baby is painful. But the other part of the curse was entering Angie's life. "Your desire shall be for your husband." There is much written on what this word from God means. Angie was about to find out. For though she didn't tell Ernesto of her newfound affection towards him, it began to show itself. Her desire turned towards him. She missed him when he was gone. She thought of him often. When the van came down the long bumpy driveway, she found herself impatient with its coming. Angie loved this man. And all that was left was to tell him.

I tend to change direction very cautiously and only after careful deliberation. I once wrote to Ernesto, early in our friendship: "Decisions freak me out, because I don't want to be unwise." This being one of the most monumental choices I'd ever faced, one that would profoundly change the trajectory of my life probably more than any other, was not taken lightly. Before I finally made up my mind for good, I was won over by small degrees. As Whitman said, "I may have to be persuaded many times before I consent to give myself really to you, but what of that?" There were a thousand little things that made me smile, warmed my heart, stopped me in my tracks at how well this man could see me. It wasn't necessarily this specific act that did it — although it was certainly a step in the right direction. But it was more what acts like these revealed about Ernesto's character. He is compassionate and generous. Like Alyosha in <u>The Brothers Karamazov</u>, *"he could not love passively; once he loved, he immediately also began to help." Ernesto does many things in a big, bold way, not least of which is love. He loves well because he is grateful for the love he's received. That overflows into everything he touches, and points to the greatest Love ever known. How could I not be drawn to him?*

The Fight

"He gave me these gifts and burdens and the history that makes me so strong and so weak, so bold and so afraid."
   -Ernesto, in an email to Angie (April 2003)

"Still here I carry my old delicious burdens... I carry them with me wherever I go."
   - Walt Whitman, in "Song of the Open Road"

She didn't tell him. The sun set on their summer and Ernesto was called back to college. He left the tree farm with no hope. She had given him no words of commitment.

He settled into his dorm and changed gears in his mind. No more eighty hour work weeks. No long drives through the country just to see her face. He had to hunker down and finish strong. He was attempting to take 21 credit hours so that he could graduate come the end of this school year. Whatever happened next, this was the last year he would be a student at the Moody Bible Institute.

He found the rhythm. A new job in the city had him working for a European importer of fine dishware and Persian rugs. The class load was large, but he had a plan for how to tackle it. He had mapped out his reading and papers on a massive calendar so he could keep up with demands.

And into this well-oiled machine came Angie on a surprise visit.

It was a great surprise. She was only in town for one day. Surely he could put his master plan on hold for a few hours. It would mean a late night and exhausted morning, but she had come to him. They had dinner at his favorite dive and wandered the streets of Chicago as the afternoon faded to dark. Finally the dark had become night, and Ernesto had to go. One of the great rules of long-distance relationships is to leave every encounter with peace. You don't want a fight as you leave one another. That fight will hang out the whole car ride home. The hurt feelings have time to grow and intensify. Ernesto knew this. Angie knew this. But it didn't stop what came next.

"Angie, it's not a big deal. It's no reason to be so upset."

"Ok." There were tears in her eyes as she sat in the driver's seat. She was trying to be strong. To put away the feelings that threatened to overtake her.

"Ok, then. So, we're okay?"

"Yeah." There was no sweetness in her answer. She was de-escalating. She was being kind. The tears still welled. Her head angled ever so slightly downward. No smile rested on her mouth. It was not okay.

"Okay. 'Cause I really have to get upstairs and hit the books. If I fall behind now, it will be almost impossible to catch up."

He stared at her. He knew it wasn't great. But it wasn't awful either. He decided it was worth it. He would let her be a little hurt now and make it up to her later. Right now the priority was school. So he nodded and opened the passenger door. He exited the car and tried to speak like everything was good and right. "I'll see you later, Ang."

By the time he reached the dorm elevators he had already moved on. His mind moved to assignments and to his plan of attack for the next four hours of study. It was 11pm now, so he would push hard until 3am. That meant just four hours of sleep. But that was doable for just one night. He could make it up Saturday morning. Yeah. That was exactly what he was going to do.

His dorm room was not meant to be lived in, but slept in. Between bed, desk, dresser, and closet, there was only a pathway for coming and going. Ernesto piled the needed books on his bed and grabbed the first of many. He sat down at the desk and was just about to enter the zone when a concern crossed into his mind. He rose from his desk and walked to the room's one window. From the 14th floor he could view the entire plaza of the school. He could see a few stragglers leaving the Student Center, and could even see the visitor's parking lot from where he had just come.

There, parked where he had left it, was the Lumina. It sat with lights off and engine cold. He knew she was crying. She was down there feeling hurt and discarded by a man who had other things on his mind. The thought didn't bring him shame. The thought instead created heat. He felt the anger rising. He knew what he had to do. He would have to go down and make this right. This was at least an hour of listening and apologizing. This was emotional energy he didn't have. He wouldn't be back up here until after midnight, and that was best-case scenario.

Ernesto spoke aloud, to no one but himself. "I don't have time for this."

His right hand clenched into a fist, and he found comfort as each knuckle cracked loudly from his rage.

He crossed the room to the phone hanging on the wall. He dialed her cell. She answered, and he could hear that she had been crying.

"Hello?"

"You still here?" It was a dumb question that he already knew the answer to.

"Yes."

"I'll be down in a minute."

"No, it's okay. You have work to do. I'll be alright." Angie was crying, it was true. But she was not angry. Sometimes emotions overtook her. But she was not one to hold a grudge or play games to prove a point. She really meant what she was saying. She would deal with this on her own, and they could hash it out later. But Ernesto was unable to stop the volcano that was rising.

"I'm coming now."

He placed the phone into its cradle. He found the sound it made quite satisfying. He picked up the phone again and slammed it back into the cradle. His head hung and he did it again, bringing the phone higher above his head before crushing it into its base. And then he was gone. The phone became brass knuckles in his hand, and he wasn't so much slamming it down as he was punching the base with it. When the phone snapped in his hand, he let it fall. He kept on punching the base, needing it to be no more. The plastic gave, and splintered into pieces. The shards tore into his knuckles and hurt. Offended by its defense, he grabbed the broken base and ripped it from the wall. Holding one end of the base, he brought the rest down upon the concrete floor, and it finally broke into many pieces. It was over. Bruce Banner was back, and Hulk was gone. His hand was bleeding freely, and he grabbed a clean sock and tied it off.

He looked like a street fighter from 20's New York. He smiled at the thought.

He crossed the plaza to Angie's car and entered as calm as the Buddha himself. She was wiping away the last of the tears, and he realized that he might be clear of this much sooner than he thought.

"Hey." He was awkward, and didn't know how to begin.

"I'm okay. I really am. I tried to call you to say you didn't have to come down. But it was busy."

"Yeah, well, you won't be able to call my room for awhile. I kinda broke the phone." He laughed as he shared this bit of information. He found it amusing, cute even.

"What?"

"I was mad, so I ripped the phone off the wall and broke it."

And that is when she saw the sock. It shone wet as the blood began to seep through its white fabric.

"You broke the phone in your room?"

"Yeah."

Her body language changed immediately. It was no longer crying girl apologizing for her tears. It was no longer sweet girlfriend. Her back straightened, and she held her head high to look at the man sitting across from her.

"You hurt yourself while beating the phone?"

"Yeah. I guess I did."

"And when you got cut, did you stop?"

He didn't like the way she was talking. He didn't like the questions. It was no big deal. Men got angry. They broke stuff. That was the way of the world.

"No. I stopped when the phone shattered."

She stared hard at him under the light of the clock tower. He didn't meet her gaze. There was astonishment and grave concern in that look. He didn't understand how he was on the ropes all of a sudden. He had come down here to make her feel better. How was he suddenly the bad guy?

She never took her eyes off him as she spoke. "Ernesto. I want you to understand something, and I want you to understand it tonight."

Ernesto finally looked back at her. He was getting angry. Who was she to tell him off? He searched for everything she was about to say. Was she going to tell him he was being childish? That he was selfish? His mind raced for countermeasures to every possible accusation she could throw. He was ready to defend himself.

She continued. "If I ever saw you lose your temper like that, and watched you beat something into nothing, I would be afraid of you."

There was nothing she could have said that would have cut him as much as those words. All defense fell away. He looked down at his bleeding hand, and a memory fell upon him.

It was late at night, and he was just a boy. His brothers all lay in their beds around him, silent but not sleeping. Outside their door, a man raged at his mother. He called her terrible names. He was screaming her into submission as she tried desperately to calm him down. She feared for her children sleeping down the hall. She feared the neighboring apartments calling the police. She feared that he might hit her again. So she was sweet and gentle, a mother talking down an infant in the middle of a temper tantrum. Only this infant was the strongest person in this house. Little Ernesto was standing by the door with a baseball bat in his hands. He had it cocked behind his head like he had learned at coach-pitch softball. He couldn't stop that man from hurting his mother. But if he came for his brothers, he would try and stop him. He would probably fail, but he had to try. As the screaming moved closer down the hall, he began to shake. He was so afraid. He could hear one of his brothers softly crying.

"I would be afraid of you." That is what she had said. His whole life he had been afraid. Afraid of angry men wielding their rage without control or enemy. For years he had been like an abused puppy. Whenever around any adult men, he would be nervous, waiting for them to unleash their teeth. As time went on, he learned how to adapt. He could mask that fear. Hide it. But it was there. And the only way he knew how to fully banish it... he had to be stronger than whoever was yelling. If he was the strongest one there was, then his rage could beat theirs.

His whole life he had known fear. As a boy, he swore he wouldn't be like these men. He had promised it. To his mother and to himself. Yet here he was. He had become the monster.

"Angie, I am so sorry."

He looked up at her. "I don't want you to be afraid of me."

Ernesto was a big man. He stood 6'0" and weighed in at 300 pounds. He was a strong man. She had watched him break unbreakable splitting mauls. If he were to lose control, she would have every right to be afraid. She had known the teddy bear. She had not known the grizzly.

She was silent, waiting for him to take the next step. Sometimes words are not enough.

"Did I ever tell you about that time I got mugged out here in the city?"

"I've heard you mention it."

"I had just come by bus back into the city. Back home, the courts had taken my little brother. My family was broken. I was... I was a mess. It was after midnight, and instead of getting a cab, I decided to walk back to campus. I just needed the air. I was walking through downtown when two men came out of the shadows. They came from different places and had me boxed in. They wanted my duffel bag. And you know what I thought when they came out of the dark?"

"No, I don't."

"I was so glad. I was glad they tried to rob me. I needed to do something with all that pain. So they came for me. And I put them in the hospital. And no one ever said a word. I was defending myself. But that ain't the truth, Ang. I wanted to hurt them. I was grateful for the excuse. The school told me I should take anger management, and I even went to a few sessions. But I never let the guy in. I was too proud."

He exhaled.

"I will go to his office tomorrow and make the appointment."

He looked up at her. Now he was the one crying.

"Angie. I swore I would never be like the men I saw growing up. And I am. I am so sorry."

It was the first time she saw him cry. And the last time she saw The Hulk.

PART THREE

SUMMER 2003

Declaration

"…While I breathe and think I must love him."
-Jane Eyre

I was screaming my lungs out at a Bruce Springsteen concert when Angie decided to tell me our fate.

I had decided to give her my sidewalk prophet, the one and only Bruce Springsteen. I learned years earlier to be very careful what songs you give to a girl. Give away too many too quickly, and you won't have none left when you finally find good love. My affection for Angie was such that I had no fear of sharing with her my favorite musician. Together we went and saw the Boss burn the Windy City down. It was a great show. It was the Rising tour, when Bruce took the national wound of 9/11 and turned it into a song we could sing to mourn what was lost. As is my custom, I sang my guts out. I didn't even mind that she saw. There was nothing left to hide now.

We left the concert and ended up on Michigan Avenue headed north. Our wandering brought us under Lake Shore Drive and onto the beach overlooking Lake Michigan.

It was a perfect night. Angie and I barely talked. We just walked together in the late Chicago night. I led us out to the edge of the water and we stared off eastward, towards home.

The concert was a great time. But the music was losing its grip on me. I loved to listen to Bruce while I was driving. Each record had a different part of the country burned into my memory. His longings were my longings. The heroic and the hopeless had always attracted me, because that had been my life. I had believed for so long that life was to be a joyless obedience. In my experience even the good stuff was covered in blood. My family was far from me, my best friends were as emotionally stunted as myself. Like Peter, I knew well the words, "Where else would I go? You have the words of eternal life." Jesus was the only good thing I had. Everything else was kind of broken.

I was a sad-sack, and Bruce does sad really well. But as I grew into a man I became hopeful. Maybe every sunset wasn't surrounded by storm clouds. Maybe we could have things in this life that were beautiful. Maybe we could know a little bit of God's goodness in the here and the now. Maybe.

It was my relationship with Angie that made me believe this. For our friendship didn't have an ugly side. There wasn't something to be overlooked. Even the hard things we went through only served to strengthen the bond. The stained glass wasn't scratched. Everything I gave came back. She was my superior in knowledge, and my equal in wit. She knew the Christ as an old friend, and that relationship was the center of her life. She was beautiful to me. So much light came from her, that I believed more beauty was possible.

Standing on the beach, I wondered how long I would get to drink deeply of this goodness. Time was running out, and soon I was set to graduate. She had given no word as to her affection. The thought of leaving her made me very sad.

"Ernesto?"

I turned to see Angie there. While I had been lost in my thoughts, she had been confirming her own.

She'd known for months that I made her laugh. And like the song says, if I could make her laugh I knew I could make her like me.

"Yeah?" I honestly had no idea what she was going to say.

She looked at me, and I looked right back at her. The traffic buzzed on behind us, and the waves crashed before us. And I knew this was either the beginning or the end. The time was right. The moment was now. She knew her will, and it was time I did too.

She spoke into the cool night.

"I'm your girl, and you're the only man for me."

I exhaled.

"I love you, Angela Kaye Sims."

"And I love you, Ernesto Moreno Alaniz."

She reached up and took my arm, and we turned back out to the water. The wind blew against our faces, and then turned back towards the shore. The wind just blows where it will, just like God's Spirit. Just like us.

Proposal

"My love has placed her little hand
  with noble faith in mine,
And vowed that wedlock's sacred band
  our nature shall entwine.

"My love has sworn, with sealing kiss,
  with me to live - to die;
I have at last my nameless bliss:
  As I love - loved am I."
  -From Rochester's Song, *Jane Eyre*

Angie has always loved France. She and her sisters always talk about their big girls' trip over there, about the art and the culture. They listen to the music of France, read the authors of France, and enjoy the food of France. So, when the time came to ask for her hand, it was to France I turned.

I worked for a high-end kitchenware shop in Chicago. I was underground, in receiving. I would go through all the rugs and linens, the fine china and glassware, and prepare them for orders. One day, while listening to a Bruce Springsteen all-day tribute, I found a book. It was not part of the inventory. Like a stowaway, it had jumped in a box in France and flown all the way to my hands in Chicago. I knew it was for Angie the moment I saw it. Angie loves

France, and she also loves paper. There was a trunk in her room housing 55 journals full of her musings and life. She loves finding wonderful stationery and having it on-hand for when the next journal finds itself full.

I thought about stealing the wonderful book. On the front, centered and transparent, was a vase of tulips. The cover was expensive and European. The smell... it smelled like the other side of the world. But I couldn't steal this thing. The gift offered at the moment of truth could not have blood on it. So I went to my boss. My boss was a cool lady. She ran the store with grace and professionalism. Her best friend in the world was her cat, and he wasn't half bad as cats go. I came before her, book in hand. "There was a journal in one of the boxes. It's not on any inventory list." I paused waiting for a response. None came. "I was wondering if I could have it."

"Yeah?" She looked up from her bookkeeping.

"Yeah."

"What you need with a blank book?"

"I am going to ask Angie to marry me, and this book is part of my plan."

She gave me a wide-eyed look of surprise. Not shock or wonder, more like she didn't think I had it in me.

"Tell you what. Get all those orders filled tonight, and it's yours."

I worked four hours after shift that night. I just stayed until the work was done. When I finally left, I was sweaty, dusty, and tired. But I had earned my reward.

I entitled the book "The Story of Us." When you open it, you will find a handwritten table of contents. If you were able to hold it in your hands and see it for yourself, you would see a list of chapters. Each chapter is an email. From the very first time we wrote, all the way to the day before the book left my hand, I documented our correspondence. Her emails were all handwritten in print, while mine were in a sloppy cursive. Reading those emails and letters told our story. From the long car ride in silence to a phone call in April that would make my intentions clear. The arc of our hearts becoming one was there for us to remember.

I've never had much money, so we didn't go out to a big dinner. I had no home or room that I could call my own, so we were once again in my mother's basement, where my couch and clothes resided. Besides, she was a private person when it came to her feelings, so this couldn't happen in some public venue. With trembling hands I pulled the book out of my man-bag. I had her sit down, and I read to her from its pages. I chose some of my favorites. I read them, and her eyes glistened with happy tears. She had given me her love, and her guard was now down.

I finished with one of my favorite lines I ever gave her. "They say it is good to be loved. I say it is good to be loved by you." I closed the book, came down to one knee, and I produced a ring. Only one person in the whole world knows the story of where that ring came from. Its history is a story in itself, one I cannot tell here. Even Angie doesn't know the story of the ring that rests upon her finger. But it is hers, and there is not another like it. This is not a style mass-produced at the malls of America, but rather a custom job shaped by a fine artisan. And the style is her. It is elegant and understated. She had no idea the ring existed. She didn't know that from the day she called herself my girl, I had begun the journey to marry her. We didn't go ring shopping. My choosing of the ring was another way I communicated to her that I knew her heart and her soul. And I offered it to her not knowing what she would say. The risk was part of the reward. Swing away.

The tears finally fell. She said yes. She took the ring and put it on her finger. I stood up before her and looked her full in the face. Up to this point, we had only held hands, and even that was still fairly new. The fire was too hot for anything else. It was my intention to honor God when it came to our love story, and I knew I was only so strong. Once I tasted of her lips I was going to be set on fire. And I could only control that burn for about six months (which is why we would marry in five). With the ring on her finger, with the answer given, I leaned forward and kissed Angie for the very first time. They say that first kisses are sloppy. That two people don't yet know each other, so there is a clumsiness to that first exchange. But we were not strangers. So that first kiss was wonderful. And they have kept growing sweeter every year since.

One Flesh

"There is no doubt in my mind that the love between a man and a woman gives both a picture and a greater taste of the love of God."
-Ernesto Alaniz

"I pity any poor married woman whose husband is not called Ernest."
-Cecil, in Oscar Wilde's *The Importance of Being Earnest*

Our wedding was two months after school ended. My boys had not yet married, and they still had the freedom to go anywhere for any reason. So they came out to the Tree Farm for one last hurrah. We spent the week preparing Rivendell for the big day. Adam, Knuth, Tony, Terry, The Toddfather, and JR put their whole life aside to come and work. We leveled a field for a parking lot. A great gazebo was constructed under the gifted hand of Bob Sims. The house was deep cleaned, lights were installed as guides to new guests, and signage was put out all the way to the highway. That week with my boys was one of the greatest I had ever shared. It was how the old world ended, and the new world started coming on.

The day finally came. All us guys slept out at the log cabin at the end of the long driveway. Knuth was making breakfast for us all, and I heard the groans of life entering the cabin. Light flooded in the many windows, and I could see right away it was going to be a perfect summer day. I rose, ate, showered, and then went and sat out on the porch. I didn't talk to the guys. There was no jovial ribbing, no one saying "It's not too late." I sat alone under a blue sky and felt the weight of the words in store for me. The vow stood before me now, and its power gave me pause. I was about to promise my life to this woman. Richer or poorer. Sickness and health. This decision would mark my entire life from this day forward. There was no reset, no $200 after rounding "Go." My prayer was then and still is today that God would kill me dead rather than let me dishonor His kingdom by breaking the vow.

I sat out there walking in the recesses of my own mind, weighing the decision. I had counted the cost, but I had to be sure. I was looking under rocks to see if there was anything I had missed. Soon her hand would be offered me, and then the two would become one. Was I willing to be with this woman forever? Was I willing to die to myself that we may live? Was I willing to love her more than myself? As I walked in that dreamscape, I could turn around and see a lever on the wall far away. I walked through rooms of toys and adventures, of playing at manhood and flirting with responsibility. I walked through my own extended boyhood and to the lever before me. It was time to leave childish things. Was I willing to grow up here and now?

It is an odd thing to write, and there are some who will think this is the musings of a fool, but it doesn't make it untrue. There on that bench on August 23rd, 2003, I grew up. It was a decision. I put my hands on the lever, and I put all my weight into it. It released and groaned forward, snapping into its new position. The decision was made. I stood up, put on a suit and tie, and was ready.

The driveway to Hidden Hollows is a quarter-mile dirt trail. It is flanked on both sides by Christmas trees at different stages of growth. The driveway does not rise and fall, but it winds and curves. From the road, you cannot see Rivendell Manor. Guests were already arriving and being seated as I made my way down its familiar path. This was the same path I walked on that dark summer night that brought me to her door. It was the same road I drove down when looking for peace throughout my college days. And this time I walked down it to take a daughter as my wife.

I stood under the great gazebo, flanked by friends and family. I stood there resolute and waited. From the house women came, escorted by men who had become brothers. Finally the wedding party was assembled. I looked down the row of men and smiled. The largeness of their personalities reminded me once again of the wonder that was my life. On top of that, it was one of the toughest wedding parties I had ever seen.

The music changed. Canon in D began to play out on the open air. The door I had knocked on those few years ago opened. And once again, there she stood. This time she wore not clothes for sleeping. This time she wore a dress of white. She came out and made the long walk, escorted by her father, one of the greatest men I have ever known. They came across the lawn and made the turn to face me. I saw her, and she saw me. I can't remember if I cried. I know I smiled. Her father offered me her hand, and I took it. We stood there face to face in front of a small crowd. I said the words and meant them. They have guided my life ever since. She said them back. I gave her a ring she still wears. And then I kissed her.

The announcement was given, and a new song played. It was the Grand Hotel Valse, from the *Life is Beautiful* album I brought her when she was sick. We didn't so much walk out as glide out. I was Roberto Benigni, and I had my Principessa. As we drove away, I wouldn't let go of her hand. I might change the radio, or scratch my head, but I would always come back seeking her hand with my own. And after years of serving God's Church, after enduring some crushing blows, after the joys of traveling the world and starting a family, we are still holding hands. She is one of God's great gifts to me. The darkness of my early poetry is all dried up. The words that come forth now are always tipped with joy. And she... she is the reason. I love you, Angela Kaye Alaniz. And I am so glad you said yes.

ABOUT THE AUTHOR

Ernesto married his tree farm girl on August 23rd, 2003. Their love has produced two children, Little Nesto and Sweet Lina. He pastors a church in America's most dangerous city, Flint MI. This is his first novella, but hopefully not his last.

If you enjoyed this story, you can read two more bonus chapters for free at ernestoalaniz.com/treefarmgirl.

NOTES

Austen, Jane. *Northanger Abbey and Other Works*. Glasgow: Caledonian International Book Manufacturing Ltd., 1998.

Austen, Jane. *Pride and Prejudice*. New York: Penguin Books, 1998.

Bronte, Charlotte. *Jane Eyre*. New York: The Book League of America, 1847.

Counting Crows. *August and Everything After*. DGC Records, 1993. CD.

Dostoevsky, Fyodor. *The Brothers Karamazov*. New York: Vintage Books, 1991.

Magnolia. Dir. Paul Thomas Anderson. Perf. Tom Cruise, Philip Seymour Hoffman, Julianne Moore, William H. Macy, John C. Reilly, Jason Robards. New Line Cinema, 2000. DVD.

Tolstoy, Leo. *Anna Karenina*. New York: Penguin Books, 2000.

Whitman, Walt. *Leaves of Grass*. New York: Mentor Books, 1954.

Wilde, Oscar. *The Importance of Being Earnest*. Berkshire: Cox & Wyman Ltd, 1994.

Made in the USA
Middletown, DE
26 May 2018